THOMAS TELFORD'S TEMPTATION

The Cutty Sark Tall Ships Race passing the 8-lock staircase at Banavie on the Caledonian Canal in 1991.

THOMAS TELFORD'S TEMPTATION

Telford and William Jessop's Reputation

CHARLES HADFIELD

B

M & M BALDWIN
CLEOBURY MORTIMER, SHROPSHIRE
1993

TO
Jack Simmons
great transport historian
to whom I owe more than I can ever repay

© Charles Hadfield 1993

ISBN 0 947712 19 4

Published by M & M Baldwin
24 High Street, Cleobury Mortimer, Kidderminster, Worcs DY14 8BY

Keyboarded by Electronic Office
4 Talbot Square, Cleobury Mortimer, Kidderminster,
Worcs DY14 8BQ

Printed by Redwood Press, Melksham, Wilts SN12 6TR

CONTENTS

ILLUSTRATIONS AND MAPS

PREFACE

John Rickman, clerk to the Caledonian Canal Commissioners, had much to do with Thomas Telford during the canal's construction. In 1819 he suggested to his close friend, Robert Southey the poet, that they should visit Scotland with Telford. Southey was an intelligent, learned and travelled man, and in the *Journal of a Tour of Scotland in 1819*[1] his account of the six weeks, written from notes made at the time, is a good one. It has especial value for us because he travelled for the whole time with Telford, whom he had not previously met, and at night, because of the limitations of the local inns of the time, they shared a bedroom.

Southey finds Telford – as many others did – personally attractive and a good companion. He writes of their first meeting on 17 August:

> Mr Telford arrived in the afternoon from Glasgow . . . There is so much intelligence in his countenance, so much frankness, kindness and hilarity about him, flowing from the never-failing well-spring of a happy nature, that I was upon cordial terms with him in five minutes. (p.7)

On 1 October they parted, and Southey wrote:

> This parting company, after the thorough intimacy which a long journey produces between fellow travellers who like each other, is a melancholy thing. A man more heartily to be liked, more worthy to be esteemed and admired, I have never fallen in with; and therefore it is painful to think how little likely it is that I shall ever see much of him again . . . (p.269).

The journey was for Telford a business one, in the course of which he inspected the works, then nearing completion (they were opened in 1822) of the Caledonian Canal, and the huge programme of road and bridge building being done under the (separate) Commission

7

for Highland Roads and Bridges, for which he was also engineer. Southey became thoroughly interested in the engineering works he saw; clearly his companion made him so. The information he records must therefore have come mainly from Telford, sometimes maybe from Rickman. Here, as often elsewhere among Telford records, one sees the great engineer paying unstinting tribute to his subordinates, notably John Mitchell, Matthew Davidson and John Gibb (ancestor of his later biographer, Sir Alexander Gibb). He was also conscious of it. Here is Telford writing to Baron von Platen from Gothenburg in Sweden on 9 September 1813:

> I trust my Countrymen will continue their activity and zeal for the Canal works . . . attention as to their food and clothing, for the ensuing Winter, is not only prudent, but, with the British, these small marks of kindness have more effect in attaching them to the Service, than things of apparently greater importance. It is by similar means I interest my several managers and Inspectors, who all consider me as their protector and friend.[2]

One sees him not only a good companion, but a relaxed organiser; the complicated journey goes well and comfortably.

The other side of the picture is that Telford so seldom mentions his equals or superiors, and Jessop* never. Southey sees several road bridges, including of course Telford's, but no other builder is recorded except General Wade, and then in terms like this for one near Aberfeldy:

> At a distance it looks well, but makes a wretched appearance upon close inspection . . . The foundations also are very insecure, – for we went into the bed of the river and examined them. (p.44)

Or over the Spey near Grantown:

> Like all the General's bridges, it was miserably constructed, and had a tremendous rise: this evil has been corrected, and the bridge itself preserved from the ruin which must otherwise speedily have befallen it – but there are tremendous cracks in two of the arches. (p.98)

He also sees many of Wade's roads, and comments on a stretch near Loch Ness:

> . . . in proceeding to Fort Augustus, and indeed in most, or all, of his roads, he seems to have, like other road makers, followed the old horse track, instead of surveying the country like an engineer. Very often he

---

* For Jessop's part in what was seen, see Chapters 6 and 7.

crosses the hill with great difficulty and labour, when both might have been avoided by keeping the valley . . . (pp178–9)

Note the word 'all' in this and the preceding quotation.

When they view the canal works, it is as if these alone exist in the world. No other canal at home and abroad is mentioned, no engineer from among the British, French, Germans, Italians, Swedes or Americans available, even though Southey himself was familiar with the canal network of the Low Countries.

Take Southey at the 8-rise staircase at Banavie, not, indeed, Telford's sole creation, for it was largely finished before Jessop's death. It is perhaps permissible to write of it as 'the greatest piece of such masonry in the world, and the greatest work of its kind, beyond all comparison' (p.203), though one's mind does go back 150 years to Riquet's 8-rise staircase at Béziers on the Canal du Midi, the locks down the Trollhättan gorge in Sweden, or indeed Rennie's 29-lock flight at Devizes on the Kennet & Avon. But when Southey continues about Banavie:

> That work is one of which the magnitude and importance become apparent when considered in relation to natural objects. The Pyramids would appear insignificant in such a situation, for in them we should perceive only a vain attempt to vie with greater things. But here we see the powers of nature brought to act upon a grand scale, in subservience to the purposes of man . . . (pp203–4)

should not someone have mentioned Hadrian's Wall or the Great Wall of China, or maybe one of the skilfully-sited great forts of Vauban?

We have, I think, now glimpsed a truth about Telford which could explain most of what I have set down later in this account. The key lies in a sentence written back in July 1783 to his boyhood friend Andrew Little: 'my disposition is not to be satisfied unless when plac'd in some conspicuous Point of view'.[3] Though he became a great engineer, it seems that he could not bear to feel that others might be his equals, indeed even his superiors.

In carrying this prepossession with him, he was helped by being a bachelor. Very much so, for he seems never to have looked seriously at a woman. Therefore he lacked, what more fortunate men possess, the sceptical eye, the less-than-enthusiastic word, with which a good wife modifies the excesses of even the most brilliant husband. He must also have possessed a rare gift: he mesmerised

9

people, compelled them in some measure to suspend their critical faculties. He did it with Southey, surely it is the key to the extraordinary behaviour of John Rickman, which we shall examine later, and after his death he sometimes mesmerised his biographers.

William Jessop and Thomas Telford worked together on the earlier development of the Ellesmere and Caledonian Canals, the second in time overlapping the first. When Professor A. W. Skempton and I had finished work on our joint book, *William Jessop, Engineer* (1979), a number of historical puzzles remained about the relative contributions of the two men to the building of these canals.

Agatha Christie's Miss Marple once said years ago at the end of a television play something like 'Your trouble, my dears, is that you believed what you were told. I gave that up years ago', and the great American physicist John Wheeler is quoted as having stated as his guiding principle: 'In any field, find the strangest thing, then explore it.' I also have, and I did. I found two strange things. The first is that too much evidence of Jessop's work seemed to have disappeared in too many places. Most remarkable is the vanishing of the whole of Jessop's personal papers, leaving not a trace behind. Several other unusual disappearances have also taken place; these I have noted as they occur in my account without trying to overemphasise them. Sadly, in total they create a formidable obstacle to one seeking only the truth which has been mitigated only in recent years by the opening of canal company records to the public. Second, that almost everyone who wrote of Telford and his canal works (I am concerned here with nothing else) appear to have accepted uncritically what Telford wrote, e.g. in his younger days to Andrew Little, in his old age in the *Life*, and in between in the papers printed and circulated at the time Pontcysyllte aqueduct was opened in 1805.

Thus I was 'led' to 'the strangest thing', the hypothesis that Telford, aided later by Rickman and later still by others whose reputations to some extent depended upon his, had over the years from about 1795 engaged in a gentle but persistent process of character erosion against Jessop, seldom by positive mis-statement, but rather by just not mentioning him when he ought to have been mentioned, and perhaps also by causing to be mislaid records that would otherwise have been kept. The motive? Surely that Jessop should not be shown to be the greater canal engineer, and that

Telford, should be regarded by posterity as the 'king' of iron canal aqueducts, and the man responsible for the creation of the Ellesmere and Caledonian Canals. It was an important claim, for Pontcysyllte aqueduct is still the highest aqueduct ever to be built in the world for a navigable canal, and the Caledonian was, in its conception and building, the biggest canal in the world, and until the opening of the enlarged Gloucester & Sharpness Canal in 1874 remained the biggest in Britain.

My hypothesis is that for 150 years he succeeded. Thinking about Telford's canal achievements has been dominated by Telford. Most historians and biographers followed his lead, and to some extent they still do, nowadays perhaps less so on the Ellesmere than on the Caledonian. The longer the imbalance of truth lasted, of course, the more time was allowed for the growth of vested interests in its perpetuation.

This book tries to set right some parts of the story: others still remain hidden, and who can ever catch up with the snowball effect of a modern myth? If I am wrong, slightly, partly or indeed wholly, I apologise to the shade of Telford, excusing myself because I feel, and long have felt, responsibility to another shade, Jessop's, to discover more of the truth about the two men and their relationship.

CHARLES HADFIELD

Chapter 1

Did it begin like this?

In January 1787, aged 29, Thomas Telford settled at Shrewsbury, sent by the influential William Pulteney to alter the castle enough to enable it to be used as a temporary residence. Pulteney, M.P. for Shrewsbury, was the younger brother of his Scottish patron, Sir James Johnstone of Westerhall. He had changed his name after in 1760 marrying the very rich Frances Pulteney, only daughter and heiress of Daniel Pulteney, first cousin of William, Earl of Bath, who died without issue in 1764. The castle was among her property. In the following year, while still working on the castle, the Shropshire magistrates engaged Telford to build a new gaol on principles laid down by the prison reformer, John Howard. Then, still with Pulteney influence, he was appointed Surveyor of Public Works for the County of Shropshire. In that capacity he began his bridge-building career with the 3-arched masonry Montford bridge over the Severn, above Shrewsbury, and then got his chance when the great flood of 10–12 February 1795 carried away Buildwas bridge and, not a county responsibility, the partly-finished aqueduct at Longdon-on-Tern on the Shrewsbury Canal. His proposal to rebuild Buildwas in iron derived, he says in his *Life*, from the existing Coalbrookdale bridge a little lower down river, and there is no reason to doubt it, but the same is almost certainly not true for Longdon (see p. 83).

Telford had begun his working life as a mason, and had gone on to take responsibility for the repair of buildings, work which included some architectural effort also, and in his spare time to study science. Now, in his new post, he would be responsible for the maintenance not only of existing publicly-owned county buildings and the design and erection of new ones, but also county bridges. Thus he entered the field of civil engineering. His post was not considered to be full-time, and he was allowed, indeed expected, to take private work as well. His opposite number in Devon, James Green, was to become a considerable canal engineer while still remaining county surveyor.

Telford must have become aware of the navigation potential of the Severn as soon as he settled in Shrewsbury, for barges and trows could reach the city when water was plentiful, and indeed sometimes moved higher still, though the river had no navigation authority nor formal navigation works. He would have been familiar with canals too, for though the canal mania can be dated from 1788, Shropshire had canals before that. Earl Gower, the Duke of Bridgewater's brother-in-law, and their respective agents, Thomas and John Gilbert, had by 1768 built and opened the 5½ mile long coal-carrying tub-boat Donnington Wood Canal from Donnington Wood to Pave Lane, and probably soon afterwards its 2-mile branch from Hugh's Bridge to Colliers End, this at first with a shaft and tunnel lift[1], later an inclined plane.

Before he came to Shrewsbury, he had on 1 February 1786 written to Andrew Little (who must have told him of some building works at home):

> The rage for building has not subsided yet I find; the neighbouring Farmers will be . . . saying (or thinking at least) who knows where this may end – our . . . descendants may behold those hillsides formed into Streets . . . and Canals cut from Sea to Sea: Dreadful Thought! That even Annandale[2] and Teviotdale are to contribute to this *growing sink of Dissipation* (and a plague on all Projectors! say they).[3]

In 1787 the ironmaster William Reynolds was building the Wombridge Canal[4] as a 1¾ mile coal- and ironstone-carrying extension of the Donnington Wood Canal, and at the same time, with Richard Reynolds, another, the 1½ mile Ketley Canal[5] to carry the same cargoes from the direction of Oakengates through a short tunnel and down an inclined plane with a fall of 73ft (Britain's first working boat-carrying plane) to the Ketley works. Both tub-boat canals were opened in 1788. A third also, begun in 1787 as a navigation level from the bank of the Severn to local collieries, was left unfinished to become the well-known Tar Tunnel.

A bigger tub-boat canal scheme, the Shropshire Canal,[6] was now originated by a group of ironmasters, led by William Reynolds. It was originally to have run from beside the Severn at The Hay, near

14

the Tar Tunnel, by two inclined planes, to join the Ketley Canal and end at the Snedshill collieries. A branch to Coalbrookdale was also planned. In the Commons, however, on John Wilkinson's, the ironmaster's, petition, it was extended by a third inclined plane to join the Donnington Wood Canal. Opened in 1792, 10½ miles long, it produced a tub-boat system some 21 miles long.

These Shropshire canals, built so quickly at the beginning of the canal mania, must have made Telford want to take part. For not just canal building was involved, but such ingenious engineering devices as tunnel-and-hoist vertical lifts and boat-carrying inclined planes.

However, not only were local ironmasters leading these developments, but also the name of William Jessop recurred: Jessop, twelve years older than Telford, a civil engineer trained by the great John Smeaton, a man already of considerable experience and also, as secretary of the Smeatonian Society, one well-known to the leaders of his profession.

Before ever Telford came to Shrewsbury, Jessop had in 1784 been asked by the Staffs & Worcs Canal company to survey the Severn and estimate the cost of improving its navigation and making a horse-towing path. He surveyed in May, and produced a printed report dated 10 August, dealing with the river below Stourport, and on 30 October another covering the section between Bewdley and Stourport. A third, reported by a bookseller but not seen by me, is dated 30 January 1786, though the MS report is dated 16 November 1785 and is taken from a survey in that month. This MS is in the Ironbridge Gorge Museum Trust's Library. It covers Bewdley–Meadow Wharf, Coalbrookdale, and includes estimates for ten locks, a towing path and other works, and of annual expenses.[7]

Now comes supposition, but likely supposition, for it is difficult to imagine that William Reynolds would not take a keen interest in any proposal to improve the Severn navigation, upon which the Coalbrookdale group so much depended. It is therefore likely that Jessop and Reynolds met. They would have had much in common, for Jessop could bring experience of Yorkshire industry and transport to match Reynolds' of Shropshire. Given a meeting in 1785 or 1786, would not Reynolds have told Jessop of the existing Donnington Wood tub-boat canal, and also of his difficulties in using horse tramroads on the steep gradients of the Coalbrookdale area?

15

And might not Jessop have replied that a dozen years earlier he had seen boat-carrying inclined planes on the tub-boat Tyrone Canal in northern Ireland[8] and suggested such planes as of possible use to Reynolds?[9] Jessop was at that time probably the only British engineer who had seen the planes, let alone been actively involved in making them operate efficiently.

Out of such a meeting may well have come Reynolds' Ketley incline of 1788, while the Shropshire Canal scheme suddenly became practicable. The invitation from Reynolds to Jessop to see the Shropshire Canal Bill through Parliament surely followed some such contact.

With Jessop surveying the Severn, and Jessop involved in the Shropshire Canal, there was no opening for the ambitious young Telford. And when, from 1789 onwards, a much bigger scheme for a canal from Shrewsbury – Telford's base – to the Mersey began to be promoted, three other local engineers were involved from the beginning, John Duncombe and Joseph and William Turner. Then, when 'an Engineer of approved Character and Experience' was wanted to take charge of the project and the Bill for what was to become the Ellesmere Canal, it was to Jessop that the promoters turned in 1791; successfully, for the canal Act was obtained in 1793.

As a major and busy engineer, Jessop would expect the appointment of a resident engineer in charge of day-to-day construction. The Ellesmere committee did this on 23 September 1793, appointing Telford General Agent and Engineer, a wide-ranging job that included administrative as well as executive duties. Rather tactlessly, considering that Jessop had been working with three engineering assistants, Duncombe and the two Turners, on the preliminaries, they do not seem to have consulted him, or even notified him in advance of their choice.

William Turner, whose engineering judgements were sounder than his mercurial temperament made them appear, then wrote to Jessop seemingly to complain that he had not been offered the job, and that in any case he did not think that one man could be both engineer and administrator. Jessop, somewhat annoyed at not having been consulted, replied:

Newark Oct. 2nd 1793

Dear Sir,

I have your letter and feel myself under some difficulty in answering it;

16

because I am uninformed of the motives which have directed the re-
solves of the Committee.

I think as you do that no one Man can properly undertake the actual direction of the whole of so extensive a concern as a Man of Art; and at the same time manage the Accompts.

I have always advised every person who has engaged in the direction of the Mechanical part of a Business of this kind not to divide his attention by interfering as an Accomptant because he may have full employment in the former if he makes the best use of his time; and others better qualified for the latter than he probably can be may have full employment also; I am quite unacquainted with Mr. Telford and with his Character; from the little acquaintance I have had with you I wish you might have the direction of that part of the Business which you have proposed to undertake and I do not think the Terms you have offered to undertake it for are unreasonable – if the Committee should consult me on this question I should tell them so, but I cannot be at the next General Meeting any that I may see or hear from in the mean time shall know my Opinion on this head and you may make such use of this Letter as you may think proper.

Yours
Wm. Jessop[10]

The last phrase was inadvisable, for it made sure that Telford himself would get to know that Jessop would have preferred William Turner as engineer. Here, clearly, is one possible cause for Telford's later attitude. Interestingly, too, the letter suggests that Telford, though he had been County Surveyor for over six years, had not till now made an impression upon the engineering world in which Jessop moved: 'I am quite unacquainted with Mr. Telford and with his Character'.

A further disappointment for Telford must have been a canal to his own town, Shrewsbury. Another Reynolds-led tub-boat canal authorised in 1793, the Shrewsbury was to take over part of the Wombridge and so be linked with the Donnington Wood and Shropshire Canals. Thence it was to run by another inclined plane, at Trench, several locks, three aqueducts (one of them at Longdon) and a tunnel to Shrewsbury, mainly to carry coal. At the first committee meeting, on 6 July 1793, it was agreed that William Jessop, or failing him, W. Dadford junior[11] should be asked to view the line of the canal and make an estimate of cost. When neither could take the job, another meeting on 14 August agreed that Josiah Clowes from the Birmingham area should be invited. He agreed.

Edward Bishop was then appointed superintendent for 'works carrying on on the Line of the Canal', and from 1 January 1794 Clowes was engaged to survey the canal four times a year and oftener if necessary at daily pay.

Then, nearly a year and a half after Telford's appointment as General Agent of the Ellesmere Canal, he appears on the scene. Clowes has died, and the abnormal floods of 10–12 February 1795 have partly washed away his uncompleted masonry aqueduct at Longdon. The committee minutes of 23 February record that Telford be asked to view the site of the proposed aqueduct at Pimley and those (probably uncompleted) at Rodington and Longdon, presumably to assess flood damage, and to attend the next committee meeting. This took place on the 28th. Telford was asked to make a plan and estimate of the alterations and additions needed to the aqueduct at Longdon, and was also appointed the company's engineer. He had at last been given charge of the canal's construction. At the following meeting the matter of an iron aqueduct at Longdon came up (see p. 82). The canal was completed in February 1797, and on 6 March 1797, his work done, Henry Williams, who had designed the Shropshire Canal inclines, was made Agent and General Superintendent.

Lastly, Telford wrote to Andrew Little on 21 October 1800: 'I go next week to arrange the Navigation of the Severn from Bewdley to Coalbrookdale'. The word 'arrange' creates a problem: I cannot trace any commission he was given at this time, and can only suppose he was researching for the article he must then have been writing for Plymley's book mentioned below.

Here, then, we have the record of Jessop in Shropshire – the Severn surveys, his involvement with the Shropshire and Ellesmere Canals, and his brief mention as prospective Shrewsbury Canal Engineer.

Telford had, nevertheless, his own standing in local society. Archdeacon Joseph Plymley, later to be the author of *A General View of the Agriculture of Shropshire* (1803) was one of those eighteenth-century clergymen whose interests went far wider than the church. He gathered round himself a group of lively men, among them William Reynolds the ironmaster, Thomas Clarkson of anti-slavery activity and Robert Townson the geologist. The group included Telford[12]. He also became a Mason and a member of Salopian Lodge 262, which his later associate William Hazledine joined in 1789. Another member was Pritchard, brother of the Coalbrookdale iron bridge architect[13]. At the end of 1800 Telford contributed a long article on 'Canals' which was printed as an addendum to Plymley's book. It covers the Severn and also the canal system as described above. Part was written in 1797, then added to in 1800. There are several references to William Reynolds, one or two a trifle fulsome; to Henry Williams and Robert Fulton as engineers; to personalities such as Thomas Eyton, John Wilkinson and the Marquess of Stafford, all concerned with canal building. But Jessop's name does not appear, not even in Telford's account of the Ellesmere Canal.

Chapter 2

The Ellesmere Canal: Lines of the Truth

For nearly two years from 1789 a group of promoters, working with three local men, John Duncombe and Joseph and William Turner, had planned, surveyed and estimated alternative lines to link the Mersey by what was later to become Ellesmere Port to the Dee at Chester and the Severn at Shrewsbury, and at the same time to generate considerable internal traffic. Between Chester and Shrewsbury, rival groups pressed the merits of alternative lines.[1]

One proposed a hilly, difficult line to serve the Wrexham collieries, the Bersham–Brymbo iron works complex, and the Ruabon and Chirk coal lands. It would then cross the valleys of the Dee and Ceiriog to reach Shrewsbury, with a branch to the Llanymynech limestone quarries. A second group wanted[2] a trunk east of the Dee, perhaps using the Chester Canal for part of the way, to Ellesmere and Shrewsbury, with a branch to Ruabon and Bersham and others to Whitchurch, Prees and Llanymynech. Such a line left the Wrexham and Chirk collieries unserved, but avoided the hills and river crossings of the western route.

The promoters now wanted 'an Engineer of approved Character and Experience'[3] to decide between the rival lines, and prepare the way for a Bill. From names suggested by Smeaton they chose the first, William Jessop, on 7 November 1791. He accepted, and was given Duncombe and William Turner to help him. It was his first offer of a major trunk canal, though already a greatly respected engineer. Back in 1789, Captain John Gell had written of him that when promoting the Cromford Canal Bill in the Lords: 'I have much dependence on Jessop if examined before the whole House. They all respect him and attend to what he says'.[4]

He put in a preliminary report in January 1792[5], and a fuller one in August[6], which said that to combine an eastern line with serving

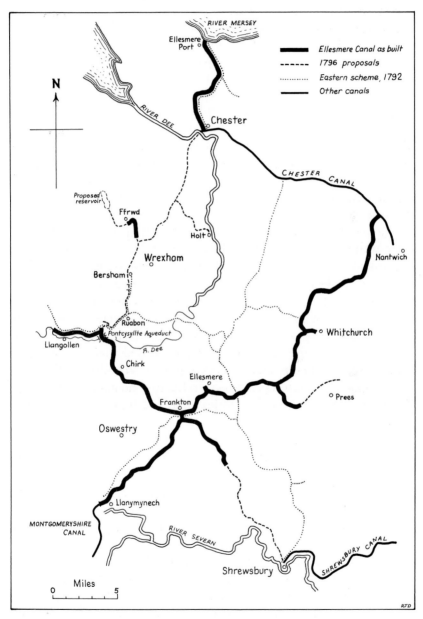

Fig 1: The Ellesmere Canal as planned and built.

21

the collieries that were to supply Chester and Shrewsbury was inadvisable, because the distance by it would make their output uncompetitive with existing supplies; therefore he favoured the western route. Basing himself on Duncombe's excellent earlier survey, he proposed a line across the Wirral from the Mersey to the Dee, and thence east of Pulford and Trevalyn to Wrexham, Bersham, by a 4,607yd tunnel to Ruabon to cross the Dee at Pontcysyllte, then by a 1,236yd tunnel at Chirk to cross the Ceiriog at Pontfaen (some ½ mile to the west of the final line), and so by Frankton, Weston Lullingfields and a 476yd tunnel to the Severn at Shrewsbury. The rise from Chester would be 303ft, the fall to Shrewsbury 150ft. Duncombe had thus identified both the crossing point of the Dee Valley and the feasibility of an uninterrupted 17-mile summit level, with a canal over the river at full height.

Jessop drew attention to what were likely to prove the two greatest engineering difficulties, the long tunnel at the level of the Dee crossing, and that crossing itself. He explained that to cross the river at the canal's planned level would cost £35,000 and require an aqueduct 970yds★ long and 126ft high. Were it to be lowered 24ft, with three locks down and up again using an 'Engine to be worked by the River Dee' to pump back the lockage water, the cost would fall to £21,286. Were no tunnelling involved, he went on, he would have liked a canal wide enough for river boats. But as internal conveyance was the great object, he proposed that the Mersey–Chester section, and possible the extension to Wrexham, should be built broad, the rest to take 70ft × 7ft narrow boats. His main line, excluding branches, was 53¾ miles long, and his estimate included

---

★ So the minute book. I had for long thought that '970yds' was a mistranscription of the original report, and that it should read '970ft', a figure near Pontcysyllte's final length of 1,007ft. Mr Richard Dean has, however, suggested to me that 970yds is correct, and that the writer was probably using the word 'aqueduct' in its broadest sense of any channel for conveying water. According to the estimate there would seem to have been a very large quantity of surplus spoil from cutting and tunnel which would probably have gone most of the way towards embanking both Dee and Ceiriog crossings at full height. Therefore the need for a large engineering structure at Pontcysyllte would not arise until later route and level alterations did away with much of the intended spoil.

There are difficulties in both solutions. Mine, that a minute book mistake of this importance very rarely occurs; Mr Dean's, that it is not easy to perceive how such huge quantities of spoil could be moved from site to destination in an orderly way. Maybe the text of the original report will some day be found; meanwhile I retain my original view that '970yds' is a mistranscript of '970ft'.

the cheaper alternative at Pontcysyllte, now put in at £21,406, including locks and water pump.

At a meeting on 10 September 1792 most of those present accepted Jessop's report, though a minority preferred the eastern line. On the 26th the committee asked Jessop, with Turner and Duncombe to help him, to reconsider the line at Ruabon to avoid a tunnel if possible. He tried to do so. Nevertheless, when the Act was passed on 30 April 1793, the same day as that for Jessop's Grand Junction Canal, Jessop having appeared before the Lords committees on both, it was for Duncombe's original line as endorsed by Jessop. Because the supporters of the eastern and western lines had now amalgamated, the Act included a clause permitting a junction between the Prees branch and the Chester Canal.

Jessop, now owning ten shares in the company, had two assistants in laying out the line, William Turner and John Duncombe, the latter having Thomas Denson working for him. But Jessop, in the middle of the canal mania, could not supervise construction. A full-time 'general overlooker' was needed, and on 19 August the committee decided to advertise for one, on the same day that they ordered William Turner to prepare plans and estimates for the aqueducts at Pontcysyllte and Pontfaen. It is surprising to find this order seemingly being given direct to Turner and not first to Jessop. Probably the latter had told the Committee that Turner should now proceed under his direction.

As we know, William Turner was bitterly disappointed when on 23 September the committee accepted Thomas Telford's application, and appointed him

General Agent, Surveyor, Engineer, Architect and Overlooker of the Works and Clerk to this Committee and the Sub-Committees when appointed. To attend meetings, to make Reports to superintend the cutting forming and making the Canal and taking up and seeing to the due observance of the Levels thereof to make the Drawings and to submit such Drawings to the Consideration and correction of Mr William Jessop or the Persons employed by the said Company for the time being as their Principal Engineer. To give instructions for contracts, to attend himself (or some confidential person by him employed) to the execution of all the Contracts relative to the making and completing the said Canal. To pay Contractors and Workmen and to keep accounts. His Engagement to extend to all Architecture and Engineering Business to the Drawing forming and directing the making of

Bridges Aqueducts Tunnels Locks Buildings Wharfs and other
works...[7]

He was to be paid £500 per year, out of which he was to pay his
assistants.

Telford, aged 36, to become an inspired road and bridge builder,
but a man at that time unacquainted with canal construction, was to
work with Jessop, rising 49, the most experienced civil engineer of
his generation. The latter, as the wording makes clear, was Principal Engineer, with responsibility for advising the committee. Telford was to execute what was required, with Jessop as a check on his
working drawings. Under him now were Duncombe and Turner.

The same committee meeting also minuted that William Turner,
'the Architect to this Concern', John Duncombe 'their Engineer',
and Arthur Davies, 'their Surveyor and Valuer' 'have by their
Abilities and diligent attention to the Interests of this Company
merited the Confidence and good Opinion of this Committee and
of the proprietors at large'.

The shareholders' meeting, however, considered Telford should
not also be clerk, and from the beginning of 1794 Charles Potts was
appointed. Telford's now became a part-time appointment, for he
continued to hold the post as Surveyor of Public Works for Shropshire. For his work on the canal he was now to be paid £300 a year,
and offer security for £5000. Meanwhile Jessop, and later Telford,
were once more to be linked with William Reynolds when in
September 1782 the Shrewsbury bank of Eyton, Reynolds & Wilkinson were appointed joint, and in October 1793 sole, treasurers to
the Company, Eyton being Reynolds' later associate on the
Shrewsbury Canal, and John Wilkinson the ironmaster.

A committee meeting on 17 January 1794, with Jessop and Telford both present, agreed to start the Wirral Canal and the branch to
near Llanymynech, especially because of the pending Bill to extend
it from nearby Carreghofa to Newtown as the Montgomeryshire
Canal. They also agreed to begin 'the building of the great Aqueduct over the River Dee'. For this

the plan of the aqueduct at Pontcysylltee with three arches as prepared
by Mr William Turner of Whitchurch, Architect, shall be adopted by
this Committee with such Alterations therein as Mr Jessop shall communicate to Mr Thomas Telford ... and that Mr Telford do prepare a
specification and proper sections and working drawings, to enable

workmen to give in estimates for erecting the said Aqueduct[8].

Jessop is shown here to be in control of design. Professor Schofield notes to me that he has known experienced draughtsmen undertake the work that Telford has here been told to do. Specifications can be repetitive, based on practical experience. They require a good, sound knowledge of construction methods and materials to produce working drawings of, for example, joints, bonding, quoins and the tricky details which the architect does not consider at the earlier stage of the entire design.

As happened on the Caledonian Canal and elsewhere, it was Jessop's practice himself to execute and sign the first construction drawings. The six surviving Ellesmere Canal lock drawings, broad for the Wirral line, narrow for the rest, were therefore probably prepared soon after the 17 January meeting, so that work could start. Three are signed 'W. Jessop 1794', the others, probably copies, are unsigned[9].

At another meeting on 31 January

> Mr Telford having stated to this Committee that he is not sufficiently prepared to enable him to advertize for proposals for erecting the Aquaeduct at Pontcÿsyltee And that he wishes to consult Mr Jessop upon various points relating to it It is Ordered that the advertizement be postponed until such time as Mr Telford shall have consulted Mr Jessop upon the Subject And that Mr Telford have Credit on Messrs Eyton and Company the Bankers for One hundred pounds to enable him to prosecute the said work at Pontcysyltee.

The extra funds were probably necessitated by the size of the job. Professor A. W. Skempton makes the point that 'this was to be a major work requiring much attention. It would have exceeded in size Whitworth's Kelvin aqueduct on the Forth & Clyde Canal (completed in 1789), the largest structure of its kind yet built in Britain'.[10]

At a meeting two months later on 31 March it was

> Ordered that the Plans Drawings and Sections of the intended Aqueduct at Pont cy syltee produced to this Committee by Mr Telford and which have been settled and approved by Mr Jessop be adopted And that Mr Telford do forthwith prepare a particular Description and Specification for the erection of the said Aqueduct and that Advertizements be inserted . . .

Contractors were then sought for this 'very extensive Aqueduct' by

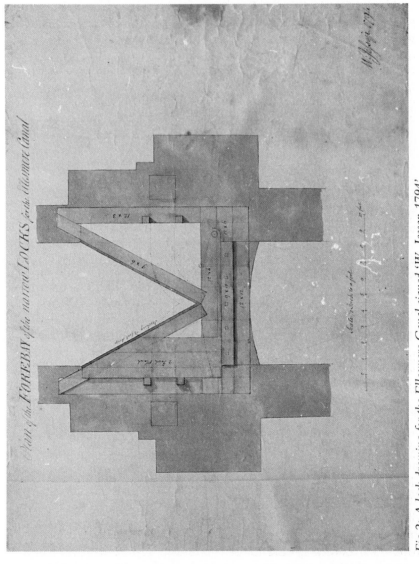

Fig 2: A lock drawing for the Ellesmere Canal signed 'W. Jessop 1794'.

26

advertisement before 24 May. Because of its later importance to the Pontcysyllte argument, I quote it *verbatim*, noting that is likely to have been drafted by Telford as General Agent:

ELLESMERE CANAL NAVIGATION
It being proposed to erect a very extensive Aqueduct, for the Purpose of carrying the Ellesmere Canal Navigation across the River Dee, at Pont cy Syltee, near Ruabon, in the County of Denbigh – Notice is hereby given, That all Persons willing to undertake the erecting and completing of the said Aqueduct, are requested to send their Proposals, sealed up, to Messrs. Potts and Leeke, of Chester, or to Mr. Thomas Telford, Architect, in Shrewsbury, on or before the 24th Day of May next; and the Committee of the Company of Proprietors of the said Canal, will attend at the Royal Oak, in Ellesmere, on Monday the 26th Day of May next, in order to open and decide upon such proposals as shall have been so delivered in, and to contract with proper Persons for the Execution of the said Work, Plans and Specifications whereof are now left with the said Messrs. Potts and Leeke, and Mr. Telford, for Inspection.

It will be expected that such Person or Persons as may be contracted with, for the Execution of the said Aqueduct, shall give sufficient Security for the Performance of the Contract.

CHARLES POTTS

Clerk to the said Company.[11]

A mason got the contract:

James Varley of Colne ... Mason, having proposed to undertake the building of the Aqueduct at Pontcysyltee upon more reasonable terms than any other person...

the committee accepted his tender. All the evidence indicates that Varley had agreed to build the masonry aqueduct designed by Turner, detailed by Telford, and approved by Jessop. Appointed, Varley started to cut and dress stone.

Meanwhile, on 21 February 1794, Matthew Davidson of Shrewsbury had been appointed Inspector of Works at Pontcysyllte, along the Llanymynech line, and of future works in the Chirk valley. A good man had come. Later, in August, Telford proposed a modified route for the canal between Pontcysyllte and Chester, which was agreed subject to Jessop's opinion.

Early in 1796 Varley must have got behind with his contract, for on 21 March the Committee 'Ordered that an accurate account shall be taken ... of the stone raised and work done by James Varley the contractor for building the aqueduct at Pontcysylte' and that he produce sureties at the next meeting for 'the due performance and execution of his contract'. There is no minute of the result, so another guess has to be made. Mine is that by now everyone was getting restless to see the Ellesmere Canal nearer completion; so it was decided to reduce the aqueduct height still further by increasing the lockage, especially since Turner had become a nuisance to the company and one whose pride need no longer be regarded. So when Jessop wrote his crucial report of 14 July 1795 recommending an iron trough at full height, he began by saying 'It had been proposed to save expence in the Aqueduct at Pontcysylte to reduce the height 50 feet and descend and ascend by Locks . . .' i.e. to 76ft. The wording 'It had been proposed' is odd. If Jessop was referring back to the committee decision of 17 January 1794, would he not have written; 'The Committee had proposed . . .'? The wording suggests a proposal with which he had not agreed; perhaps one made by the leading men without a formal meeting.

What height had the contractors who answered the advertisement been told the aqueduct was to be? In his preliminary report of January 1792, Jessop had said one of 126ft would be needed, but in that of August that it could be lowered to 102ft by using three locks at each end and pumping back. Given Jessop's position, one would expect Turner to design roughly to that height. That he did so is supported by Telford's own rather muddled account in the *Life* which refers to piers and arches nearly 100ft high (see p. 101), and by the drawing, probably Telford's, of an iron aqueduct (see p. 89) which shows one of about 100ft.

Once Telford had been appointed general agent, Jessop would have more time to do fundamental thinking. On the one hand, the problems to be solved had greatly changed; on the other, Jessop, now the leading engineer of the canal mania[12], was more experienced than when he had written his 1792 reports.

Let us look at Jessop again. Particularly important were three other canals, the Bills for which he was principal engineering witness and had seen through Parliament: the Grand Junction, Grantham and Rochdale. For all three he ensured that water supplies sufficient for commercial success would be made available. The Grand Junction (30 April 1793) from the Thames at Brentford to Braunston, was to have two summits, and therefore two reservoir systems; the Grantham, indeed, authorised on the same day, was to be the first English canal that could be supplied entirely by reservoirs; while Jessop's success in getting the Rochdale's Bill through Parliament (4 April 1794) depended entirely upon his extensive reservoir provision. So we can take it that after his success with all three, the lesson learned was that without provision for good water supplies a canal Bill would fail. Separately from these, Jessop had on 10 December 1792 formally entered into partnership with Benjamin Outram and two others in the Butterley iron-works[13]. Thenceforward he became more and more interested in the uses of iron, and, with Outram to consult, more able to get a second opinion.

Again, between 1792, when he had proposed a 4,607yd tunnel on the Ellesmere's original main line, and 1794 Jessop had learned much more about the difficulties of canal tunnelling as compared to those of increasing lockage and summit water supplies. Applying the results, he had successfully eliminated Rennie's tunnels on the Rochdale and the Kennet & Avon[14], and had struggled with those that were inevitable, Butterley on the Cromford, Braunston and Blisworth on the Grand Junction. These experiences must have confirmed him in the committee's wisdom on 26 September 1792 in pressing him to get rid of his long tunnel near Ruabon.

On his own Ellesmere Canal, the beginning of the problem Jessop set himself to solve can be seen in a clause in the original Act which opened the possibility of a junction with the Chester Canal from the Dee at that city to Nantwich as soon as the Ellesmere had reached Frankton. This was made greater when on 17 January 1794, with Jessop and Telford both present, the committee agreed to start the branch past Llanymynech. This, as Jessop would at once have realised, involved seven falling locks, to which a liability for four more on the Montgomeryshire might be added. Moreover, the construction of the first four (Frankton) locks would enable the canal onwards past Hordley to Weston Lullingfields and so to Shrewsbury to be started, all with falling locks and yet more water to be drawn from the direction of Pontcysyllte. Where was this greatly increased amount of water to come from? The Ruabon line was still being discussed, but even were it to be settled quickly and satisfactorily, he would be for some time to come largely dependent upon his envisaged great 400-acre reservoir between Coed-Talon and Llanfynydd on the river Cegidog, and then speedy construc-tion of the branch down which water could be run to the main line at Pontcysyllte. There were, of course, small secondary supplies available, but not enough were all the envisaged developments to take place.

One can imagine that someone as experienced on water supply as Jessop would have decided, perhaps even before he had got up from the committee table, that of the possibles, only one solution attracted him; Pontcysyllte aqueduct must be build to the full height of 126ft, so that supplies could be run from the Dee using an intake higher up, and taken over the structure as the main supply for the Shrewsbury and Llanymynech lines and if necessary the Chester Canal link. A great deal would be needed. Locks at either end of the aqueduct to reduce its height were no longer an option.

Jessop, I suggest, went away to think. But before that, he probably saw John Duncombe, who had worked with him since 1791 and had on 23 September, at the meeting at which Telford had been appointed general agent, been described as the concern's 'Engineer', and asked him to suggest how he would build a full-height masonry aqueduct. Duncombe did so. Dated April 1794, it had three tiers of arches, one inverted[15]. Meanwhile, Jessop probably decided, no harm would be done by saying nothing more, but not stopping stone cutting for Turner's structure; it was bound to be needed whatever was built. Telford, too would be getting on with negotiating for a better line between Chester and Pontcysyllte.

In July 1795 Jessop reappeared, having now been told by Telford that a revised Chester line had been agreed. So a water route from the Cegidog and the great reservoir should in time be available. But meanwhile? On 14 July 1795, from Shrewsbury, perhaps after a conference with Telford there, Jessop wrote a report[16] to the chairman of the committee which approved, except in one place, Telford's resurveyed line. He recommended that the flight of locks down from Plas Kynaston quarry to Pontcysyllte should be 'gradual and be disposed in regular distance to near that Aqueduct', and that a branch should be built to near the Acrefair collieries. He also proposed to raise Bala Lake 6in to augment the supply available to the Dee until the aqueduct could carry supplies from his intended summit reservoir. As for the proposed Whitchurch branch–Chester Canal link, this he thought had better wait until construction on the main line and branch had made water available. So soon had the old eastern line reinstated itself; it was to grow quickly in importance.

We see Jessop here anticipating a very considerable need for water from the completed main line to Shrewsbury, the Llanymy-

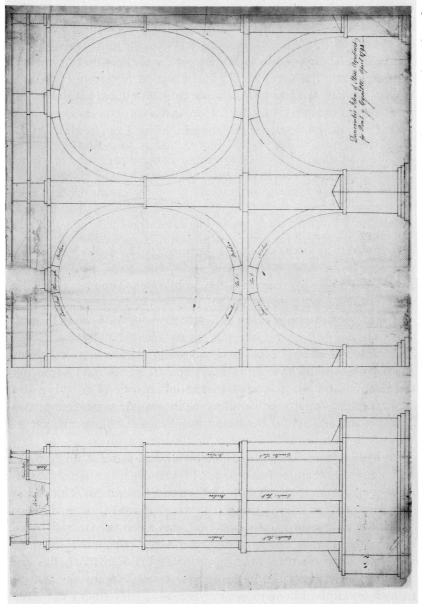

Fig 3: John Duncombe's proposal for a full-height masonry aqueduct. The caption reads: 'Duncombe's Idea of Stone Aqueduct for Pont y Cysilte April 1794'.

31

nech line, and the likely Chester Canal link, one that would need not only all the water he could get from the Cegidog, but also the Dee. Indeed, he thought the Dee would not provide enough; hence his suggestion to raise the level of Bala Lake, itself the Dee's main supplier.

Thus a full height Pontcysyllte became inevitable. If so, how was it to be built? Masonry? Possibly; perhaps at Shrewsbury, Jessop had shown Telford Duncombe's drawing, and asked his opinion of a full-height masonry aqueduct. Here is his view, as set out, many years later, in the first unedited version of his *Life* (see pp. 100–1)

> ... to Lock down each side as originally intended I perceived was quite inadvisable, as it would have been losing Water on both sides the Valley, whereas there was not more than sufficient to supply the general Lock-age from the Summit level. To construct an Aqueduct upon the Plan previously practised by Masonry Piers and turning Arches, at nearly 100 feet in height, of sufficient width and strength to afford a Puddled Water Way would have been an expensive and hazardous operation . . . .

He would probably have added; 'and much more so were the structure now to be at full height'.

Thus, with masonry ruled out, what was left? My own view is that William Jessop of Butterley ironworks had already chosen iron. While he had been away, he had probably discussed it with his partner Outram, whose single span iron trough at the Holmes on the Derby Canal was to be completed in February 1796, only a few months later, which itself might well have originated with Jessop himself, and so back to Reynolds and Telford at Longdon (see p. 83).

Perhaps also he had visited Coalbrookdale to see William Reynolds before meeting Telford in Shrewsbury. The latter would most certainly have told Jessop all about his excitement with Longdon, and perhaps shown him his sketch of an iron aqueduct (see p. 89). If so, that calm man might well have been taken aback as he contemplated such a hair-raising structure, even more so as he imagined it raised from Telford's 100ft to his own 125ft. But not overly so, for by now he must long have known the answer: an iron trough, certainly, but on masonry piers, using the stone Varley was still busy cutting. He would then have told Telford what he envisaged, whereupon that skilled worker in stone would at once have seen himself building those exciting piers, while his new-found enthusiasm for iron would have full scope in solving the problems that would arise when the time came to design and erect the trough.

So Jessop went on with his report of 14 July 1795:

It had been proposed to save expence in the aqueduct at Pontsycylte to reduce the height 50 feet and descend and ascend by Locks, but in due consideration I must now recommend to the Committee to make this saving by adopting an Iron Aqueduct at the full height originally intended which on correcting the Levels appears to be 125 feet above the surface of the water of the River Dee.

The advantages that will attend the preservation of this Level are too obvious to need explanation. The arches or rather openings of the Aqueduct may be seven of 50 feet each the remainder may be raised by an embankment, and this embankment will be formed by Earth to be boated from the cutting between the Dee and the Chirk valley – as few hands can be employed in this mode of Working, and it will of course take much time in the Execution, no time should be lost in beginning it.

It was originally proposed to cross the Chirk Valley a little above Chirk Bridge but from an objection by the owner of the land, the Line was altered to cross at Pontfain. It would still be very desirable to adopt the first Idea, and if instead of an embankment of Earth, which would shut up a view of the valley, it be crossed by an Iron Aqueduct I should hope the objection might be removed as instead of an obstruction it would be a romantic feature in the view and avoid damage to much of the Meadows and the Plantations on the Banks of the valley, and miss a very expensive and hazardous part of the line on the steep Banks on the South side.

Meeting on 10 August, a fortnight after the foundation stone had been laid, the committee minuted:

The report of Mr William Jessop principal Engineer to this company dated the fourteenth of July last . . . having been now read and taken into consideration. It is ordered that the line of the said canal extending from the River Dee to Pontcysyltee . . . recommended by Mr Jessop . . . should be adopted and the Clerk . . . is hereby directed to give . . . public notices [previous to a Bill].

They continued:

Mr Jessop having represented to this Committee that in order to pre-serve the level of the said Canal and prevent delay and loss of water by locking up and down to the Aqueduct at Pontcysyltee it will be advisable that the said Aqueduct should be constructed of Iron at the level of one hundred and twenty five feet above the surface of the water of the River Dee and that the arches or openings of the Aqueduct should be seven in number of fifty feet each and the remainder of the valley shall be raised by an embankment. It is ordered that the recommendations of Mr Jessop in that respect shall be adopted . . .

We may note here that the committee approved an iron trough for Pontcysyllte, and ordered 'that the recommendation of Mr Jessop in that respect shall be adopted and the General Surveyor and Agent to this Company is hereby directed to proceed in the said works conformably thereto.' They added an order that surveyors should prepare a drawing and section of the Chirk valley line to take account 'of the improvement proposed by Mr William Jessop in passing the said Valley by means of an Iron Aqueduct . . .' Therefore Pontcysyllte had been formally authorised: Chirk in iron had not, pending the necessary surveying and levelling, and the landowner's consent, because it lay outside the 100yds limit of deviation specified in the Act.

The laying of the foundation stone (for the wording see p. 48) on Saturday 25 July 1795, between Jessop's report and the committee's agreement, is reported in the *Salopian Journal*. The newspaper writes that 'it is expected that the work will go on with much expedition, as a great part of the materials are already provided', a phrase that seems to refer to the now discarded low-level masonry aqueduct, for which less stone would have been needed. The implication is also that news of Jessop's proposed use of iron had not yet reached Shrewsbury's newspaper.

We must now backtrack to follow the water supply story. Before Jessop had mentioned the use of Bala water in his report of 14 July 1795, he must have known that clause 91 of the original Ellesmere Act prohibited the drawing any water from the Morlas, Ceriog or Dee, or from any brooks supplying them, between 15 June and 15 September in any year, sometimes at other times also, in the interests of Chester Waterworks, unless their proprietors gave their consent. Therefore it was urgent, once the full-height aqueduct had been authorised, either to make a special arrangement with the Waterworks Company, or to draw upon Lake Bala. A long look at the complexities of Section 91, together with another at the seemingly haphazard organisation of the Company, must have ruled out the first alternative. So Lake Bala it must be.

34

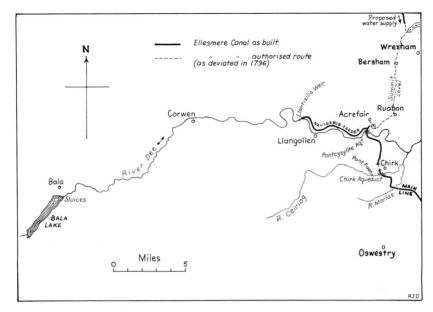

Fig 4: Jessop's water supply problem and its solution.

The Committee took the point, the same meeting that authorised the aqueduct also deciding that permission to draw upon Bala as 'an occasional reservoir' should be sought from Sir Watkin Williams Wynn, who owned it and much land round it.[17] On 21 March 1796 the committee approved a draft clause to empower the Company

> to take water for the supply of the canal and collateral cuts from any brooks or streams now flowing into the River Dee, and to return a sufficient quantity of water out of Bala Pool in order to supply any such water as may be so taken out of the brooks or streams now flowing into the said River Dee, and to make use of the said Pool as a regulating reservoir . . .
>
> Mr Jessop is desired to attend Sir Watkin Williams Wynn with a copy of the said clause for his consideration.

Sir Watkin was at that time a minor. Probably his Trustees felt the matter could wait until he could decide for himself. When he did, it was in favour of Jessop. However, for the time being Sir Watkin would not agree to such Parliamentary powers. The intermediate steps are well set out in Dr Cohen's thesis and need not concern us here.[17] On 29 June 1803 the Ellesmere Company's committee resolved that a feeder from the Dee to the aqueduct should be built, with an intake 'above Llangollen', an equivalent amount of water being returned 'into the ancient channel of the River Dee'. Sir Watkin was again approached, and in April 1804 agreed. For a modest rent, he would allow the company to raise Bala's level, '1 foot higher on the surface that it usually falls to in the dry weather in summer', by means of a regulating weir near Bala Bridge.[18] A Bill, piloted through Parliament by Jessop, received the Royal Assent on 29 June 1804. The feeder, now made navigable, was finished at the end of 1807, though the Bala sluices, essential to satisfy Chester Waterworks, were built by Telford and ready before the aqueduct was opened in November 1805. The whole operation, originating with Jessop's July 1795 report, proved a remarkable example of farsighted planning.

With the reasons why Jessop had in his report of July 1795 proposed a full-height aqueduct now clear and followed through to their sequel, let us return to the period immediately afterwards.

The discussions which had taken place in Shrewsbury were continued by letter after Jessop's return to London when, on 26 July, he wrote to Telford:

> In looking forward to the time when we shall be laying the Iron Trough on the Piers I foresee some difficulties that appear to me formidable – In the first place I see the men giddy and terrifyed in laying stones with such an immense depth underneath them with only a space of 6 feet wide & 10 feet long to stand upon the same want of room will hardly allow space for the Beams and scaffolding while the Iron work is putting together –
>
> I therefore think in the first, that in order to reduce the weight of the Iron, or the parts of it – it will be better to have the openings narrow by adding another Pier, so as to have 8 openings of 52 feet from Centre to Centre instead of 60 feet.
>
> In the next place I would have the Piers 7 feet wide at the Top* instead of 6 feet, and make them about 2 feet more in the other dimensions.
>
> I hope you will not have proceeded with the other Foundations till you received this.
>
> And I begin to think it may be better to have the Canal 9 feet wide & 5 feet deep, as was first intended . . .[19]†

---

* Actual width is 7ft 4in. It seems certain that Jessop and not Telford decided the final dimensions.

† This being the only surviving letter from Jessop to Telford about their work together on the Ellesmere Canal, I asked Professor Schofield for his opinion of the two men's relationship. He replied: 'Although language here is polite (and why not?) this letter of WJ to TT is a clear instruction. Telford is being told.'

As regards the remark about foundations, it seems likely that, until Jessop's report could be considered by the committee, no official change could be made. Therefore the foundation stone of the masonry aqueduct had had to be laid the day before this letter was written, even though the two engineers were redesigning the whole structure.

The proposals accepted in August 1795 were for much more embanking and a much shorter aqueduct – perhaps some 500ft in all, against 1,007ft as built.

The same meeting of 10 August also approved the resurveyed line from Chester to Pontcysyllte (subject to Telford's asking Jessop for clarification upon the water supply to the summit) and for the Whitchurch branch, and finally ordered parliamentary notices to be published preparatory to a Bill.

In October William Turner, who since the beginning of the year had been no more than a shareholder, issued a statement criticising the revised route to Chester, and suggesting alternatives. He and Jessop having then gone over the line again, the latter reported hurriedly from London on 8 December 1795.[20]

Two canal Acts resulted in 1796. The first abandoned the old Whitchurch branch, and substituted a new one, with branches from it to Prees and Ellesmere. It also required the Ellesmere Company within two years to seek an Act to join the Chester. The second authorised the revised route from Pontcysyllte to Chester, with branches to Acrefair and Talwern collieries, and the great Coed Talon reservoir. Jessop appeared in Parliament on both, supported on the first by Denson, on the second by Telford and Denson, this being Telford's first appearance before a Lords committee.

No work was thereafter done on the Pontcysyllte–Chester section except to build 2⅓ miles of the Ffrwd colliery branch, begun 1796, though various ideas, including using inclined planes or substituting a railway, were afterwards aired. The lack of drive behind it may have been, partly at any rate, the result of the internal explosions in the Wilkinson empire around this time. It was formally interred in Jessop's report of 24 January 1800.

By now it had become clear that the true future of the company lay in the development of its central coal-limestone-lime exchange, and in the prospective link with the Chester Canal. The branch from Frankton past Llanymynech to Carreghofa was opened in 1796, to be extended in 1797 for 16¼ miles to Garthmyl when the first part of the Montgomeryshire opened. It was followed by Frankton–Weston in 1797. In February of that year work also began on the realigned branch towards Whitchurch and the Chester. That, and the completion of the Frankton–Chirk collieries line, were now priorities, with access to the Ruabon collieries over Pontcysyllte coming next. By 1801 the Whitchurch line had reached past Ellesmere to Bettisfield, and two miles of the cut through Whixall Moss had been opened to drain it. In 1801, also, the Chester Canal junction at Hurleston had been authorised; it was to be completed in 1805.

Let us now follow the story of the aqueducts from where we left it at 10 August 1795. On 9 September the committee was told that John Simpson was to join Varley as co-partner of the Pontcysyllte work, a new contract to be drawn up. So far Varley had been paid £2,002, so he must have prepared and cut a good deal of stone. In October, Telford reported that 'the Aqueduct at Pontcysyltee is carrying on with all the dispatch that a work of that magnitude will admit of'[21] and on 26 November it was

> Ordered that the Embankment at the south end of the Aqueduct at Pontcysyltee and the cutting along the adjoining Bank and towards Chirk valley which is necessary to form the said Embankment shall be carried on under the direction of Mr Telford and agreeable to the directions in Mr Jessop's report...

By the opening of the year 1796 wartime inflation was beginning to bite, money was coming in more slowly, and costs had begun to rise. These factors influenced action upon major projects like the two big aqueducts.

Back at Pontcysyllte, an undated letter from Telford to Matthew Davidson, in charge of aqueduct construction, who received it on 14 January 1796, says 'I have daily expected your drawing of the Iron Aqueduct*, and was anxious to have it before the meeting of the Committee, which is to be held on the 13th – If you can possibly let me have it before Wednesday next, it will do ...' A little puzzling? If Telford has done the original, why lend it to Davidson without keeping a copy? But if it were Jessop's then it would be natural for Davidson as superintendent to be studying it.

Telford must have recovered it, and then got on with detailed

---

* He seems to be saying 'your (copy of the Jessop) drawing of the Iron Aqueduct...'

preliminary drawings, for he writes again to Davidson on 7 October 1796:

> I have here sent you the Geometrical Drawing* of Pontcysylte, I have left the foundations to be put in on the Spot, and according to their depth – the number of Piers are likewise undetermined. –
> The perspective drawing will be ready in a Weeks time.

On 20 January 1796 contractors had been appointed for Chirk; John Simpson again, with William Davies and also William Hazledine, the ironmaster of Shrewsbury, this to be finished by 1 October 1798. In February Outram's iron trough at the Holmes was ready, in March that at Longdon on the Shrewsbury Canal (see p. 86). Nevertheless, it took Hazledine and Telford less than a month to conclude that the difficulties of giving Chirk an iron trough were too great,† for on 15 February Telford, writing to Matthew Davidson, said: 'I have seen Mr Jessop as to the Aqueduct at Chirk, and he agrees as to the general principle of the adopting Brick or Rubble Arches instead of an Iron Trough . . . .'[22] Maybe Longdon and his Buildwas road bridge had taught Telford how much was still to be learned about iron. He was not the only one. On the Peak Forest the proposed iron aqueduct at Marple was scrapped after Fulton left in September 1795; instead, Outram built the fine masonry structure we have today.

Work at Chirk was delayed while the aqueduct was redesigned. It seems first to have been planned as a plain masonry structure[23]. Only later was it decided to build the spandrels of the arches with longitudinal walls, and then to lay a cast-iron bottom for the water channel across them, the sides being made up of ashlar masonry backed by bricks. In his report of 27 November 1799 Telford tells us that its arches had been completed, and that 'proposals for the Iron Plates, which are to form the bottom, have been received, and

---

* Professor Schofield considers he means the setting-out drawings. These would be based on an accurate land survey to provide a longitudinal section on the centre line of the aqueduct. Only general details, dimensions and centres of the piers would be shown on such a drawing, and depths of foundations could only be determined on site. We may note that these would have to be very precise, because with a masonry aqueduct small discrepancies, (e.g. at Marple where there are discrepancies up to 18 ins between adjacent piers) were acceptable, this would not be the case when, as at Pontcysyllte, prefabricated iron trough construction was being used.

† Mr Richard Dean suggests another possibility. The landowner's consent to the design was needed, because the aqueduct lay outside the permitted deviation line. Richard Myddelton may have preferred a traditional stone bridge.

they will be provided and laid early next Summer'[24]. Two days later, Hazledine of Shrewsbury's proposals for 'furnishing plates and screws' for Chirk was agreed. Jessop then had a look at it, and in January wrote:

> The masonry of Chirk Aqueduct is very perfect. I have seen no reason to recommend any deviation from the design . . .[25]

Chirk, opened at the end of 1801, is 696ft long and 70ft high; it has 10 arches of 40ft span, a navigable width of 11ft, a width of masonry each side of 5ft 6in, and a water depth of 5ft.

A report dated 25 November 1801, seemingly Telford's, described the now completed aqueduct as different from any other:

> . . . there is no earth or puddle made use of; the waterway is formed with a cast iron bottom, and square masonry on the sides; the spandrels of the arches are hollow. By this mode of construction, a very considerable proportion of the masonry is saved in the breadth of the Aqueduct; the risque of expansion or contraction from puddling is avoided. In case of any leakage, the water may find its way through the spandrels, without injuring the Work; and every part of the masonry, and the bottom of the waterway, may be readily examined at all times[26].

As for Pontcysyllte, little was done for several years. On 10 February 1797 the committee minuted to enquire 'upon what terms of Mr John Wilkinson and Mr William Reynolds will either jointly or individually agree to furnish the Iron Work for Pont cy syltee and fix up and complete the same' – an interesting minute, for by excluding Hazledine it suggests that the Plas Kynaston foundry near the aqueduct's north end, which was to be the key to success, was not yet available[27]. The responses must have been discouraging, for on 28 June the committee ordered that proposals should be advertised, though I have not traced any such advertisement. And then work was suspended to expedite that at Chirk. Not until 17 November 1799 did Telford report to the General Assembly that 'As soon as the season will permit that the masonry be taken in hand, I have recommended, that the Abutments and remaining portion of the Piers of Pont Cysylte Aqueduct should be begun upon'. At the same time the committee ordered the remaining mason's work at Pontcysyllte to be advertised.

In his report of 24 January 1800, Jessop tried to deal with the problem of how to get coal from Ruabon on to the southern canal lines across Pontcysyllte, now that the main line to Chester had been abandoned. He proposes a railway from the collieries to the aqueduct, and then puts alternatives: should the railway 'be continued over the columns intended for the Aqueduct, or whether the Aqueduct should be completed to communicate with the Railway on the north side of the river'. He inclines towards bringing the railway over the piers, and goes on:

> In the execution of the columns, I would recommend, that, in what remains to be done, they should be built hollow, and be composed of stones well worked to two feet in bed, and be connected one side with the other, at every six feet in height, by two pieces of oak (dovetailed a little on the underside) principally for the purpose of internal scaffolding. The courses thus put together, will be less liable to false bearings than if they were solid; it will save five or six hundred pounds in the expence; and what to me appears most material, it will afford safety to the workmen.
>
> Instead of wing walls connected with the abutments at the ends of the embankments, it will save some expence, and perhaps have a better appearance, if the abutment, built of rough masonry, and connected by bond timbers, with a counterfort about 12 feet in length, and 7 feet in thickness, be buried in the slope of the earth, terminating the embankment; the earth, so sloping, will bury near a half of the next column, which half may, of course, be built of rough masonry. The whole of the sides of the embankment should be planted, which in time, would become not only ornamental, but profitable.
>
> I cannot leave Pont Cysylte without saying that the columns, without any exception, are executed in a more masterly manner that anything of the kind that I have before seen.*

These structural recommendations seem all to have been carried out, that to build hollow above a certain height being crucial, because it reduced the load on the foundations.

The piers, 20ft × 10ft at base tapering to 13ft × 7ft 4in at the top, were built hollow above 70ft, but using crosswalls instead of cross timbers. The embankment was brought forward, and the abutment has very short wing walls with the counterforts extending right down to the base of the foundation. The decision to extend the aqueduct to its full eighteen piers and to shorten the approach embankments (though leaving a 500yd embankment on the south side) must have been taken before Jessop wrote, and probably in the light of comparative estimates for the cost of bridging or embank-

---

* A remark that pays tribute to Telford's ability as a Master Mason.

ing[28] for immediately after his report, on 5 February 1800, the committee accepted John Simpson's tender to complete the piers and abutments.

Jessop's half-hearted suggestion[29] that the piers might be used for a railway instead of a canal was considered, but on 25 November 1801 the committee decided in favour of a canal, Telford then being told to prepare drawings and specifications for it. By that time a good deal of work had been done, for in his report for the same meeting Telford wrote:

> During the last year and a half, five Piers have been built from the foundations up to the level of one hundred and ten feet above the common surface of the river Dee★. Nine other Piers have been raised twenty-three feet in height, which has brought them up to the same level; there are five other Piers which require twenty-three feet each to raise them to the before-mentioned level.†

It was probably only now that, in consultation with Hazledine, the final design for the trough was settled. Given that the piers were being built, the ironwork had to be designed to fit. It seems likely that Hazledine, his foreman Stuttle, and Telford did this in consultation, Telford supplying information such as loadings. The specialist Hazledine would then have prepared detailed drawings down to the bolts, support trusses and thickness of metal of the component parts based upon the anticipated loads, all in consultation with Telford. These done and, we can assume, approved by Jessop both as engineer and ironmaster, a price would be agreed, and his tender of 17 March 1802 for executing and erecting the ironwork then accepted, this to be supplied from his new Plas Kynaston foundry. Thereafter Hazledine would proceed with full responsibility for casting and then erection, Telford servicing him by providing temporary work such as access roads, scaffolding, and perhaps lines, levels and general checking. The contract completed, the entire works would be checked by Telford for quality of workmanship, line and level and any defects put right. We can expect that Telford kept Jessop in touch with progress, probably by contacts made during the Caledonian Canal works, and that he himself would have made one or two checks, perhaps one when

★ Probably the string course level.
† In fact, the aqueduct has eighteen, not nineteen piers.

42

briefing himself for the 1804 Bill, and one nearer completion of contract.

That the major contribution was Hazledine's seems to be confirmed by surviving papers held by the Institution of Civil Engineers showing Telford's much later involvement with the masonry aqueducts with iron internal plating (especially Slateford) of the Edinburgh & Glasgow Union Canal. Telford, consulted, does not show detailed knowledge of Pontcysyllte's ironwork, and in 1818 James Thomson is sent down to talk to Stuttle and get the necessary details. Meanwhile, William Davies was building the southern embankment to a maximum height of 75ft.

In 1803 it was decided to build a coal-carrying railway from Ruabon to Pontcysyllte, and to seek an Act for a water feeder up the valley past Llangollen to an intake from the Dee at Llantisilio. In October of that year the committee asked Jessop to survey and report on the whole line, especially on the progress of the Chester Canal connection, and the proposed Shrewsbury connection, Pontcysyllte, and water supply. There is no record of his doing so, other than the evidence he gave on the 1804 Bill, when he proved the preamble and produced the estimates, while Telford gave evidence on the financial position of the company. That, and his regular contacts with Telford on Caledonian Canal business, probably served the same purpose. Nevertheless, as so often with other enterprises, Jessop was more closely involved with the men working on them than ever appears in records. On 8 January 1804 Telford proposes to Jessop the names of those to be appointed to senior jobs on the newly-authorised Caledonian Canal, among them John Simpson off the Ellesmere. Of the latter Telford had written a few days earlier to John Rickman the Clerk: 'He [Jessop] can examine Mr Simpson an Eminent and reputable Builder, who has examined these matters very carefully, and with whom Mr Jessop has been acquainted for many years'[30]. Against his name Jessop wrote: 'I know Mr Simpson well'.

Telford's report of 1804 says:

> The Iron-work of the Trough-part of the Aqueduct of Pontcysylte over nine Arches, is now put up, being nearly one Half of the whole Length; many Plates being now cast and brought to the Bank at the North-end of the Aqueduct – The Workmen being familiar with the Operations of putting the Plates together – and the operations at the foundry being in a very regular Train, and well supplied with Metal, there is reason to

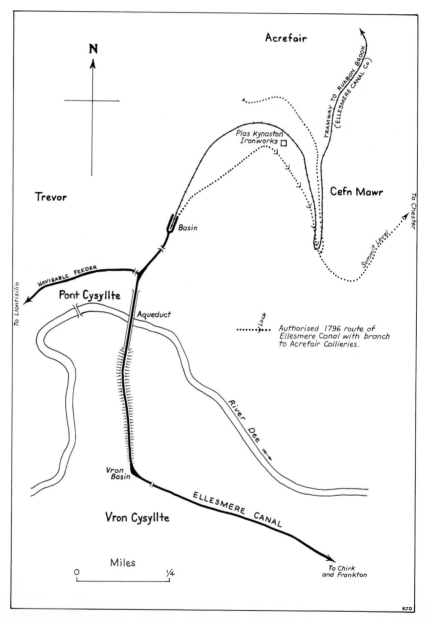

Fig 5: Lines planned and built around Pontcysyllte Aqueduct.

expect that the whole of the Trough-Part will be completed about Midsummer next. Timber has been provided for a Part of the Towing Path, which will be put up early in the Spring, as well as the Iron Railing to protect it.

The Earthen Embankment and Lining for the Canal, is carrying on by Means of three Iron Railways; and it is proposed to have this Part finished at the same Time with the Aqueduct[31].

The cutting of the navigable feeder upwards from Pontcysyllte to Llantisilio was authorised in 1804 and practically finished in 1806. Meanwhile, on 26 November 1805, the aqueduct had been opened with much ceremony. Jessop was not there; he never did attend such ceremonies, seemingly too busy with the future to concern himself with the present or past. His job was done.

Chapter 3

The Ellesmere Canal: The Offering of Temptation

This day the stupendous aqueduct of Pontcysylte, upon the Ellesmere canal, was opened with great solemnity. This aqueduct passes over the River Dee, at the eastern extremity of the romantic and well-known Vale of Llangollen. The morning threatened to be unfavourable; but, before noon, the day cleared up, and the sun shone, adding, by its lustre, to the beautiful sight of various carriages, horsemen, and persons, descending, by every road, path, and approach, leading towards that great work. Before 2 o'clock, the aqueduct having been filled, the procession began. The earl of Bridgewater's barge led the way, in which was his lordship and the countess; sir Watkin Williams Wynne, bart. sir Foster Cunliffe, bart. col. Kynaston-Powell and lady, and several other ladies and gentlemen. In the prow of the barge, the serjeant-major of the Shropshire volunteers, in full uniform, carried a flag, on which was painted a representation of the aqueduct, the Dee, and the valley, with the following inscription:

'Here conquer'd Nature owns Britannia's sway,
While Ocean's realms her matchless deeds display.'

Next followed other members of the committee, and Mr. Telford, the projector of the aqueduct and general agent to the company, in col. Kynaston-Powell's barge, carrying two union-jacks. In the third was the numerous band of the Shropshire volunteers, in full uniform, playing 'God save the King,' and other loyal airs. The fourth boat was filled with numerous ladies and gentlemen, with agents, clerks, and the heads of the departments employed in the execution of the work, and decorated with a handsome flag, on which was inscribed,

'Success to the iron trade of Great Britain,
Of which Pontcysylte aqueduct is a specimen.'

The fifth and sixth boats were filled with various persons, crowding, with anxiety, to have the satisfaction of thinking that they had been amongst the first to pass the aqueduct. As soon as the first barge entered the cast-iron water-way, which is 126 feet above the level of the river Dee, the artillery company of the Shropshire volunteers fired 16 rounds, from two brass field-pieces, which were taken at Seringapatam, and presented to that regiment by the earl of Powis. In the intervals of the discharge from the guns, the procession received the repeated acclamations of the numerous workmen, and a prodigious concourse of spectators. As the barges entered the basin on the north end of the aqueduct, five waggons, drawn by one horse, and containing two tons of coal each, the produce of Mr Hazledine's collieries at Plaas-Kynaston, were brought along the iron railway, and deposited upon the wharf, in order to their being (with more, which had been previously brought there) loaded into two boats, which had followed the procession for this purpose. The company from the barges landed, and the earl of Bridgewater, as chairman of the committee, conducted the ladies and their friends to a house belonging to the company, where they partook of a cold collation; after which, Mr Hunt, of Boreatton, one of the committee, delivered an eloquent and impressive oration, explaining the origin and object of this work, and drawing a comparison between this and the ancient and modern aqueducts. The company went back to their barges, and the procession returned in the same order as it came. The two boats laden with coals followed the procession; the first having a handsome flag, thus inscribed:

'This is the first trading-boat which passed the great aqueduct of Pontcysylte, loaded from Plaas-Kynaston collieries, on the 26th day of November, 1805.'

The discharge from the guns, as the procession returned, the plaudits of the spectators, (calculated at full 8000) the martial music, the echo reverberating from the mountains, magnified the enchanting scene; and the countenance of every one present bespoke the satisfaction with which they contemplated this very useful and stupendous work. – From the aqueduct, the committee and their friends proceeded to the inn at Ellesmere, where upwards of fifty gentlemen, with a number of their most respectable tenants, who had been invited, sat down to a sumptuous dinner, with the earl of Bridgewater as chairman; and, after much loyalty and conviviality, on his lordship's retiring, his health was immediately given, not only as chairman of the committee and meeting, but as lord of the extensive and rich manor which gives the name to this canal; as a worthy successor to the father of British canals, and as an active promoter of the improvements in the agriculture, commerce, and manufactures of Great Britain. That every person might be apprised of

47

the dimensions and magnitude of this work, a card was distributed, previous to the first passing the aqueduct, containing as follows:

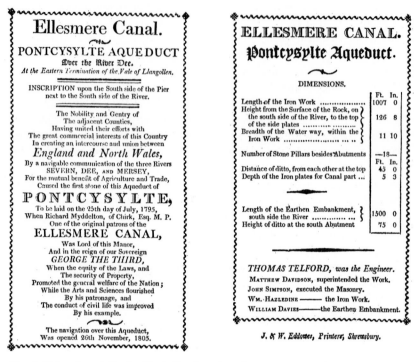

Ellesmere Canal.

PONTCYSYLTE AQUEDUCT
Over the River Dee.
At the Eastern Termination of the Vale of Llangollen.

INSCRIPTION upon the South side of the Pier
next to the South side of the River.

The Nobility and Gentry of
The adjacent Counties,
Having united their efforts with
The great commercial interests of this Country
In creating an intercourse and union between

England and North Wales,
By a navigable communication of the three Rivers
SEVERN, DEE, AND MERSEY,
For the mutual benefit of Agriculture and Trade,
Caused the first stone of this Aqueduct of

PONTCYSYLTE,
To be laid on the 25th day of July, 1795,
When Richard Myddelton, of Chirk, Esq. M. P.
One of the original patrons of the
ELLESMERE CANAL,
Was Lord of this Manor,
And in the reign of our Sovereign
GEORGE THE THIRD,
When the equity of the Laws, and
The security of Property,
Promoted the general welfare of the Nation;
While the Arts and Sciences flourished
By his patronage, and
The conduct of civil life was improved
By his example.

The navigation over this Aqueduct,
Was opened 26th November, 1805.

ELLESMERE CANAL.
Pontcysylte Aqueduct.

DIMENSIONS.

	Ft.	In.
Length of the Iron Work	1007	0
Height from the Surface of the Rock, on the south side of the River, to the top of the side plates	126	8
Breadth of the Water way, within the Iron Work	11	10

Number of Stone Pillars besides Abutments	—18—	

	Ft.	In.
Distance of ditto, from each other at the top	45	0
Depth of the Iron plates for Canal part ...	5	3

Length of the Earthen Embankment, south side the River	1500	0
Height of ditto at the south Abutment	75	0

THOMAS TELFORD, was the Engineer.
MATTHEW DAVIDSON, superintended the Work.
JOHN SIMPSON, executed the Masonry.
WM. HAZLEDINE ——— the Iron Work.
WILLIAM DAVIES———the Earthen Embankment.

J. & W. Eddowes, Printers, Shrewsbury.

Fig 6: Printed card (both sides) distributed to those present at the opening of the Pontcysyllte Aqueduct 26 November 1805.

At Pontcysylte, during the procession, a couple of sheep were roasting near the Aqueduct, on which, with an ample addition of beef and ale, the numerous workmen were to dine in the adjacent foundery, where the iron- work was cast. The Artillery company and band of music were plentifully regaled both at Pontcysylte and Ellesmere.

So runs the account under the date of 26 November 1805 in the *Annual Register*, at the time a widely distributed and respected magazine of record, into which, to save exact repetition, I have inserted the text of the card to which it refers. One assumes that Telford, General Agent of the company, prepared the card and had it distributed, and then wrote this account. Who else? Jessop is not mentioned.

48

The aqueduct's opening was taken as a suitable moment for the committee to report to a shareholders' meeting on the present state of the canal's affairs. The meeting was held on 27 November at Ellesmere, and the Report was later printed along with Rowland Hunt's oration at the opening ceremony. In the absence of evidence to the contrary, it is reasonable to assume that the Report also was written by Telford as General Agent. Printed in 1806, it was widely circulated.[1]

The Report is detailed, covering 43 printed pages. Neither Jessop nor Telford is mentioned: immediately, Thomas Denson is made Resident Engineer, with 'Thomas Telford, for some years to come, twice in every year, to examine and report upon the state of all the Canal Works, and point out what occurs to him, not only with regard to the works, but as also to the general interests of the Company'. Denson is to be paid £150 p.a., Telford £100 p.a. Part of the Report is taken up with a financial statement, and here we do find:

William Jessop, for sundry surveys, journies, inspections, plans, estimates, and for attending Parliament at several times, including his expenses

£1103.18.0.

Later Telford is described as 'general agent' for accounts purposes.

Rather oddly, on a page to itself, this paragraph ends the Report:

CONCLUSION

HAVING now detailed the particulars relative to the Canal, and the circumstances of the concern, the Committee, in concluding this Report, thinks it a justice due to Mr. Telford, to state, that the works have been planned with great skill and science, and executed with much œconomy, precision, and stability, doing him, as well as those employed, infinite credit.

BRIDGEWATER,
Chairman.

Then follows a Letter to the Right Honourable The Earl of Bridgewater, from Rowland Hunt, Esq. It is separately paginated. It contains personal tributes to many of the promoters of the Ellesmere Canal, and then a description of the opening ceremony

REPORT

TO

THE GENERAL ASSEMBLY

OF

The Ellesmere Canal Proprietors,

HELD AT THE ROYAL OAK INN,
ELLESMERE,

On the 27th Day of November, 1805.

TO WHICH IS ANNEXED,

THE ORATION,

DELIVERED

AT PONTCYSYLTE AQUEDUCT,

ON ITS FIRST OPENING, NOVEMBER 26, 1805.

Printed by Order of the General Assembly,

THE RIGHT HONOURABLE

THE EARL OF BRIDGEWATER,

Chairman.

Printed by J. and W. Eddowes, Shrewsbury.

MDCCCVL

Fig 7: Title page of the Report of 1805 to which the Oration was annexed.

50

including the procession of boats over Pontcysyllte aqueduct. Here he writes:

> The complete sense of security, in which we floated 126 feet above the River Dee, and a just acknowledgement to Mr Telford, to whom it was deservedly a proud day; and who had most happily arranged the whole of our accommodation, as well as constructed the wonderful Edifice that supported us, naturally united with the above.'

Then follows the Oration itself, seemingly not much altered in its printed form, and splendid it is. Rowland Hunt had been on the canal committee from 1791, and chairman until 1803, when he was succeeded by the Earl of Bridgewater. Having ranged the world, Mr Hunt's oratory settles upon Pontcysyllte:

> Here fully acknowledging also the services and fidelity of our other professional or commercial connections of the Company, we will mention, as concerned in the scientific and practical construction of the works, our General Agent, Mr Telford; who, with the advice and judgement of our eminent and much respected Engineer, Mr Jessop, invented, and with unabating diligence carried the whole into execution. I am happy to understand, that we may expect from him such an account and description of Pontcysylte, as will hand down to posterity, and convey to distant countries, (like the History of the Edystone Lighthouse, by Mr Smeaton) a memorial of its excellent construction, and of its public utility.
>
> In such a history will be found deservedly mentioned, the names of Mr Hazledine, the spirited founder of the Duct itself; of Mr Simpson, the accurate mason, who erected the pillars; the well-computed labours of Mr Davies, who constructed the mound or tunnels adjacent; and the careful and enlightened inspection of Mr Davison,[*] who overlooked the whole: – I cannot, however, decline looking back to the early labours of our late ingenious and zealous servant Mr Duncombe; nor should I omit the name of his relative Mr Denstone,[†] who, with habits of prudence and regularity peculiar to himself, has essentially promoted the interest of the proprietors.
>
> Certain I am, that the noble, liberal, and spirited defenders of their country who surround me, will approve, while I record, that one thus employed, Mr Hazledine, while engaged in an undertaking which would have absorbed the time, the attention, and the capital of almost

[*] Davidson.
[†] Denson.

any other man – yet found resources, in an active and patriotic disposition, to lead and instruct the very artificers who cast the materials or erected this Structure – *in the practice of arms* – for the internal defence of that country, which he was enriching by the result of his and their labours.

Thus will Pontcysylte stand for ages, a Memorial of the active loyalty of those who were sedulously industrious in its creation, and will record the eminence of Patriotism, as well as Progress of the Arts, both of which have been so successfully patronised by our beloved Sovereign.

Hunt knew it all. Here, quite correctly, he refers to Jessop as 'Engineer' and Telford as 'General Agent' – Telford the Agent and site engineer, Jessop the Engineer for the project. He goes on to recognise not only Simpson, Davies and Davidson, but also the early men on the work, Duncombe and Denson, and then Hazledine, whose men 'cast the materials or erected this Structure'.

The Oration is followed by an Appendix. It begins with two pages which almost exactly reproduce the wording of the card that was distributed on opening day. Here they are again.

INSCRIPTION

AQUEDUCT of PONTCYSYLTE,

OVER THE RIVER DEE,

At the Eastern Termination of the Vale of Llangollen; on the Side of the Pier next to the South Side of the River.

The Nobility and Gentry of
The adjacent Counties,
Having united their efforts with
The great commercial interests of this Country
In creating an intercourse and union between
ENGLAND AND NORTH WALES,
By a navigable communication of the three Rivers
SEVERN, DEE, AND MERSEY,
For the mutual benefit of Agriculture and Trade,
Caused the first stone of this Aqueduct of

PONTCYSYLTE,

To be laid on the 25th day of July, 1795,
When Richard Myddelton, of Chirk, Esq. M. P.
One of the original patrons of the

ELLESMERE CANAL,

Was Lord of this Manor,
And in the reign of our Sovereign
GEORGE THE THIRD,
When the equity of the Laws, and
The security of Property,
Promoted the general welfare of the Nation;
While the Arts and Sciences flourished
By his patronage, and
The conduct of civil life was improved
By his example.

The navigation over this Aqueduct
Was opened 26th November, 1805.

The wording differs slightly from the original inscription, still in place. 'Severn' should be 'Severne', 'Pontcysylte' should be 'Pontcysyllty' and '1795' should be 'M,DCC,XCV'.

The last two lines are an interpolation, and do not appear on the original.

ELLESMERE CANAL.

PONTCYSYLTE AQUEDUCT.

DIMENSIONS.

	Ft.	In.
Length of the Iron Work	1007	0
Height from the Surface of the Rock, on the south side of the River, to the top of the side plates	126	8
Breadth of the Water way, within the Iron Work .	11	10
Number of Stone Pillars besides Abutments . . .	—18—	
	Ft.	In.
Distance of ditto, from each other at the top . .	45	0
Depth of the Iron plates for Canal part	5	3
Length of the Earthen Embankment, south side the River	1500	0
Height of ditto, at the south Abutment , . . .	75	0

THOMAS TELFORD, Engineer.

MATTHEW DAVIDSON, superintended the Work.
JOHN SIMPSON, executed the Masonry.
WM. HAZLEDINE, ——— the Iron Work.
WILLIAM DAVIES, ——— the Earthen Embankment.

CHIRK AQUEDUCT.

DIMENSIONS.

			Ft.
Number of Arches			10
Length, including Abutments			696
Height from the Surface of the Meadow, to one foot above the level of top Water, in the Aqueduct			65
Width across the top of the Aqueduct . . .			22
Length of the Base of each Pier, at the Surface of the Meadow			32
Breadth of ditto			12

The only difference is that 'Thomas Telford, was the Engineer' has become 'Thomas Telford, Engineer'.

Then follows (pp 33–36) a 'Copy of some Minutes, from the Book of Orders of the General Assembly'. These mainly cover the company's beginnings, seemingly in order to list its early promoters and committee members, and show Rowland Hunt's service from the beginning. Extracts are listed from minutes of 28 June and 31 August 1791, 6, 10 and 25 September 1792 and 3 and 17 July 1793. Then follows a final extract from the General Assembly minutes of 27 November 1805. The series ends with:

> Ordered, That the Thanks of this General Assembly be given to Rowland Hunt, Esq. for his very able Oration, at the opening of the Aqueduct, at Pontcysylte, on the 26th instant, and that the same be printed and annexed to the Appendix to the Report.
>
> BRIDGEWATER.

Bound up with these two separately paginated sets of papers is the Davies and Jebb folding map of 1796, here hand-coloured: *A Plan of the Ellesmere Canal, and its collateral Branches united the Rivers Severn,*

54

Dee & Mersey and the several Canals connected therewith. A slip tipped in on the back of the map reads:

> This Statement would have been laid before the Proprietors some weeks earlier, but for the disappointment of a supply of paper for the publication, which was experienced by the Printers. February 25, 1806.

We have here an intriguing series of documents, all bound together for generous circulation: Report; Hunt's letter; Hunt's Oration; aqueduct inscription and factual summary; the 'Copy of some Minutes'; Map; and its slip. Let us take each in turn, adopting the hypothesis that Telford wanted to use the occasion to draw attention away from Jessop and towards himself. The Report only mentions Jessop in the accounts, and there gives him only passing reference. The second and third, Hunt's Letter and Oration, make up between them a history of the canal's promotion and construction, with special reference to the aqueduct. Hunt had been on the canal committee two years and more before Telford had been appointed, and knew the relevant facts; we may take it that he could not be influenced. So we can regard it as accurate, balanced also as regards the two engineers.

We continue. Why is the Report's Conclusion, signed by the Earl of Bridgewater, paying tribute only to Telford, given such emphasis before the two Hunt documents? The Earl had not the knowledge of the past that Hunt had, nor was Telford to be ignored in the two Hunt documents – a generous tribute is paid in the Letter, where he only among engineers is mentioned, and in the Oration, along with Jessop and others. One supposes that the purpose was to encourage the reader to get Telford's name fixed in his mind before reading what Hunt says.

Then, after the Letter and Oration, follow the reproduction of the original aqueduct inscription, with opening date added, and then the factual summary.

The discrepancies with the Oration are obvious. Jessop as 'Engineer' and Telford as 'General Agent' have been replaced by Telford alone, now 'Engineer'. The tributes to the two precursors, Duncombe and Denson, have gone, with only Telford's own subordinates left; and Hazledine is now credited only with 'executed the Iron Work', and not with also having performed the most difficult job of all, erecting the iron trough upon the masonry

55

piers★. I confess that I find especially regrettable this devaluation of Hazledine's astonishing achievement from Hunt's generous tribute to him and his 'artificers who cast the material or erected this Structure' down to 'executed the Iron Work', and in the accounts still further to 'for iron work'. With this printed and widely circulated summary which overrode what the former chairman of the company that employed him had said, Telford did not wait for future historians to inscribe his name upon the annals of Shropshire and of canal engineering history; he did it himself. So doing, myths were launched that have survived for two centuries.

After the summaries follow the straightforward minute book extracts, the useful map, and then the slip apologising for late circulation of the whole printed collection. Maybe harmless. But let us reflect. The aqueduct was opened on 26 November 1805 before 8000 spectators, but the Oration itself seems to have been delivered only to members of the Canal Committee and probably their guests. The rest of the crowd had received the card, which must then have passed from hand to hand as the story of the great aqueduct's opening was told and retold.

Owing to the printers' failure to order enough paper, three months elapsed before anyone, even committee members, was able to read any facts about Pontcysyllte except those on the card, which included those vital words: 'Thomas Telford was the engineer'. Yet J & W Eddowes were the city's biggest printers, and publishers of its weekly newspaper.

One gets an impression of planned urgency. Why? What were the forces that led this able and, to our knowledge, upright Scot not to be tempted, for we all experience that, but to succumb? Two offer themselves.

As Jessop had initiated the Ellesmere Canal, so Telford had the Caledonian in 1803. (For the story see Chapter 6). Government favoured it, and by early 1804 he was hoping to be made engineer, with Jessop as his adviser. Instead, a few short months later, he found himself junior under Jessop as senior engineer, with residents working under both. His reputation as a canal engineer had carried insufficient weight to counterbalance that of the immensely more experienced older man. Though left to take charge of a huge programme of Highland road and bridge building, by the autumn

---

★ Note also that in the accounts that form part of the Report the payment to Hazledine of £17,284.17.5½ is only described as 'for iron work'.

of 1804 he must nevertheless have been left a much disappointed man. Then came what he probably regarded as a flattering invitation, one, perhaps to soothe a badly bruised ego.

A few months before Pontcysyllte's opening, the main line of the Grand Junction Canal was completed, 93½ miles long, then with 110 broad locks and two great tunnels from the Thames near London to join the Oxford Canal at Braunston and so provide a water line to the industrial Midlands and the Trent. By then, too, important branches had been built, like that to Paddington on the edge of London. William Jessop had been principal engineer from its Act in 1793 to its completion on 25 March 1805, except for a space in 1797–9[2], and by 1805 was at the peak of his career as probably Britain's greatest civil engineer.

Shortly before completion, the committee reported to the company's General Assembly on 4 June 1805 that

> it would afford great satisfaction to the Public, as well as the Proprietary, to learn the actual state of the works of this National Undertaking from the unbiassed Judgement and Report of an Engineer hitherto totally unconnected with the Concern. For that purpose your Committee selected Mr Telford, whose professional character ranks high, and whose opinions deserve to be received with attention and consideration.

Telford's report was dated 3 June, six months before Pontcysyllte was opened. It made recommendations for increasing water supply, but otherwise found nothing seriously wrong, the committee commenting that the principal matters to which he alluded (except for water supplies) had been anticipated and in fact acted upon[3].

Given that Jessop and Telford had then begun work on the Caledonian, it seems likely that, even if Jessop did not suggest Telford's name, it would not have been chosen had Jessop been unwilling to accept it. Here was Telford, probably for the first time, going carefully over a major trunk canal built by his senior on the Ellesmere, one to be so successful that it was to pay a good dividend in the first year after full opening.

It must have been obvious to him that to Jessop (along with his resident James Barnes) would go the credit for what was soon to be known as the Great Grand Junction. Disappointed on the Caledonian, was he now tempted beyond his determination to resist, to make sure that Jessop, and those who had worked with him, should not also be given the credit for the Ellesmere and especially Pontcysyllte? Some such reaction might account for the wording of those documents I have quoted which were not Rowland Hunt's own. And, having been so tempted and given way, did he not find that he had boxed himself in regarding his whole future attitude to William Jessop?

William Hazledine remains. For he, unlike Davidson and the others, was not a subordinate, but a considerable ironmaster with a foundry at Shrewsbury as well as his new one at Plas Kynaston, while his elder brother John ran the Bridgnorth foundry with its links with Trevithick and Rastrick. Why then should Telford feel diminished, as seemingly he did, by Hazledine's skill in successfully performing the formidable task of erecting Pontcysyllte's iron troughs, an achievement at which we, looking up at the great aqueduct nearly two hundred years later, can still marvel? It was, after all, what he had contracted to do, and even lavish praise would in no way have lessened Telford's own success. Have we here a symptom of what was suggested in the Preface, a fear of any other great man within his own range of work, just because he was great?

It says much for William Hazledine, six years younger, that he continued to work with Telford on the Caledonian Canal and, much later, on the Menai Bridge.

Chapter 4

The Ellesmere Canal: The Making of the Myth

Thus myths were created. Such used to be born from antiquity, but the invention of printing changed that. In our own day we watch their creation for good reasons or bad and, once created, their persistence. Some with which we are concerned still persist; others have been, or are being eroded. I hope in this and the following chapter to suggest why they began and then persisted for a century and a half. The first: that Telford was the canal's engineer. Chapters 2 and 3 will, I hope have set out the true state of things, that stated by Rowland Hunt.

Until the setting up of British Transport Historical Records after nationalisation in 1948, few original canal records were easily accessible, though such other sources as local newspaper files and collections of printed or manuscript canal documents could be discovered by the persevering. Before then, and sometimes after, Telford's biographers* mainly used three sources, the 1805 papers we have already examined, the Little letters, and Telford's *Life*, published in 1838.

Telford's letters to his schoolfriend in Scotland, Andrew Little, have long been known. Samuel Smiles[1] used them and Alexander Gibb[2] transcribed them. The originals still remain in private hands, but to date they have never been photocopied, and students unable to examine them are dependent, as I am, upon the Gibb transcriptions.† They cover the years 1780–1803, and contain little germane to our subject, but that little has been crucial to biographers' judge-

---

* In this chapter I shall quote as necessary from Telford's principal biographers, to show their influence upon history. In Chapter 5, however, concerned with certain aspects of the story in more detail, I shall not so quote, but leave readers to examine the texts for themselves. They are all reasonably accessible.
† The versions included in Gibb's book are not identical to the transcriptions.

Fig 8: Thomas Telford – print from a portrait painted by Samuel Lane and exhibited at the Royal Academy in 1822.

Fig 9: William Jessop: a portrait painted c. 1805.

ments. These will be quoted as they occur. Here is Telford writing to Andrew Little from Shrewsbury on 29 September 1793:

My literary project is at present at a stand, and may not unlikely be retarded for some time to come as I was last Monday appointed Sole Agent, Architect and Engineer to the Canal which is to join the Mersey the Dee and the Severn, it is the greatest work, I believe, that is now in hand, in this kingdom, and will not be completed for many years to come, you will be surprised that I have not mentioned this to you before, but the fact is that I had no idea of any such thing untill an application was made to me from some of the leading Gentlemen, and I was appointed at their meeting, tho' many others had made much interest for the place. I cannot be said to be confirmed untill after the general assembly of the Proprietors which is to be held on 31 Octr. tho' 'tis not likely that that meeting will do away with the act of a numerous Committee of the leading Men.

This is a great and laborious undertaking but the line which it opens is vast and noble and coming in this honourable way I thought it too great an opportunity to be neglected . . . . Mr Pultenay approves much of it, as do all my friends, it will require great exertions but it is worthy of them all, there is a very great Aqueduct over the Dee, besides Bridges over several Rivers, which cross the Line of March.

He wrote again on 3 November:

I duly received yours of the 6th Oct. but agreable to your request I deferred answering it untill I could let you know the determination of the general meeting of the Ellesmere Canal Navigation, which was held last Wednesday. They have confirmed my appointment as general Agent the Salary is 500£ a year, and I have to keep one clerk and one confidential foreman which I have to pay out of that sum and my travelling Expenses will of course be considerable, but I have reserved the right to carry on such of my architectural business as does not require my personal attendance, so that I shall retain all I wish for of that, which are the public buildings and Houses of importance. The other parts of our business are better to be without. They give a great deal of unpleasant labour for very little profit in short they are like the calls of a Country Surgeon. Those I shall give up without reluctance, except what relates to Mr Pulteney and Lady Bath and I have the pleasure to say that they are not disposed to quit me. You will not be surprised that altho this employment was offered to me, that there should be many who looked forward to it with anxious eyes and that they had endeavoured to raise a party at the general meeting, but we were too powerful for opposition. I am fortunate in being on good terms with most of the leading men whether by property or abilities and on this occasion I had the decided support of the great John Wilkinson king of the Iron Masters, who is in himself an host. I travelled in his Carriage to the Meeting and found him much disposed to be friendly . . . .

Davidson* is Canal mad and there will now be occasion for all his exertions, for besides the real labour that attends such a great public work, Contentions, jealousies and prejudices are stationed like gloomy sentinels from one extremity of the Line to the other, but as I have heard my mother say, that an honest man might look the Devil in the face without being afraid, we must just trudge on in the old way . . . .

Given that Telford was writing excitedly and proudly to an old friend a long way away, we cannot treat either letter as accurate history; they convey human feelings. Why not? So my historical comments should be taken lightly.

On the first letter, I find it difficult to credit Telford's statement that 'he had no idea of any such thing' until some of the leading gentlemen approached him. To learn that an important and lucrative engineering job linked with his own city was in prospect, and not to be interested, strains credulity. I suggest he approached Pulteney, his patron, and Wilkinson, whom he knew, to declare his interest in applying for the post, and then answered the advertisement (see p. 16) The job specification he gives Andrew Little is unexceptionable, 'Sole Agent, Architect and Engineer' is a shortened version of that in the company's minute book. At the second letter, let us smile and pass on.

There is, however, another contemporary source, for at this point Telford found an admirer in Kathleen Plymley, sister of the author of the survey of Shropshire[3]. She met Telford early in November 1793, and was attracted, as were so many others;

> . . . he has by uncommon genius & by unwearied industry raised himself to be an excellent Architect and a most intelligent and enlightened man, his knowledge is general, his conversation very animated, his looks full of intelligence and vivacity. He is eminently chearful and the broad Scotch accent that he retains rather becomes him.

Is there a touch here of Telford's mesmerising effect on others, considering it was a first meeting? She goes on:

> . . . he has just received a very advantageous appointment, the entire

---

* Matthew Davidson was already working for Telford.

management of the canal that is to form a junction between the Severn, Dee and Mersey.

One does raise an eyebrow – no more – at 'entire management', a phrase that can only have been derived from Telford.

The background to Telford's *Life* and its editor, John Rickman, is given in Chapter 10, and to save readers' time they may like to read it before they go any further. We now have access to three versions of the *Life*. Telford's first draft, authentic because in his remarkably firm handwriting; second, a redraft, still in his handwriting, but with emendations by his editor. Deletions cannot of course be identified with certainty, but most of the handwritten changes can be attributed either to Telford or Rickman. Third, the printed version which appeared over four years after Telford's death, further changes in which must be attributed to Rickman alone. All three can be consulted in the library of the Ironbridge Gorge Museum Trust. We can date Telford's drafts as written between 1803 and 1834, Rickman's work at about 1834 towards publication in 1838.

It should be noted that until recently the printed text has been accepted as being Telford's. But this is far from being the case in certain crucial respects. Therefore the book requires from us two separate studies; the extent to which Telford himself modified the truth about Jessop; and the extent to which Rickman added to these modifications on his own responsibility before and after Telford's death. In the following pages I have tried to do this for the sections on the Ellesmere Canal.

The first version, headed *The Ellesmere Canal*, begins

The time was now arrived when my professional pursuits were to be in a great measure changed. – Since the Duke of Bridgewater had about the Year 1760, introduced Canal Navigation, it had made considerable progress in various parts of the Kingdom, and had been partially adopted in Shropshire. – The advantages to be derived from this mode of conveyance, did not escape the attention of the most enlightened of the Country Gentlemen, who formed the determination of having this rich and thriving district of Country accommodated by Canal Navigation, so as to unite the rivers Severne, Dee, and Mersey; for this purpose, they had the County Surveyed, and a scheme formed, – and so violent, at that time, was the rage for Canal speculation, that at the first general meeting, a Sum four times the estimated expense, was, without hesitation subscribed; and an Act of Parliament obtained in the Year 1793.

Then follows a description of the route, after which he writes:

> In carrying a Canal along the borders of North Wales, and afterwards on the Summit which separates the Counties of Salop and Chester, altho' there are advantages in procuring Water, and in distributing it . . . yet obstacles arising from irregularities of Surface and deep Valleys were to be encountered. –
>
> When the Companys business was so far arranged, as to require the commencement of practical Operations, the Committee of management, composed chiefly of County Magistrates, having at the Quarter Sessions observed the county works were conducted, were pleased to propose my acting as General Agent to this extensive and complicated Undertaking.
>
> Having naturally a stronger disposition for the management of Works of simplicity and magnitude, than for the complicated details of House Architecture, I therefore did not hesitate to accept their offer; and from that time directed my attention to civil Engineering.
>
> As the most expensive Canal Works, consist chiefly of Masonry and Carpentry, my previous avocations had qualified me to conduct them, in Earth work (also an important consideration,) I had the advantage of consulting Mr William Jessop an experienced Canal Engineer, on whose advice I never failed to set a proper Value.

There is here a blend of *suppressio veri* and *suggestio falsi*. The absence of any lead-in, including Jessop's employment to survey, to get the Bill through Parliament, and to lay out the line, his position as Principal Engineer, or the instruction given Telford to seek Jessop's approval for all drawings, are all omissions. The last sentence quoted, however, is a *suggestio falsi*, for it implies that Telford was in charge of the works, and only needed to consult Jessop on earthwork. One notes also that a seemingly generous tribute to a colleague does divert attention from the possibility that Jessop had also been concerned with such structures as locks and aqueducts.

This original was redrafted; mostly in Telford's still very firm hand. A considerable number of alterations were then made to the redraft, mostly by Telford in a more sprawling but not at all shaky hand, and one or two, I judge, made later by Rickman. The result was almost identical with the printed text. In the following extracts I have italicised the alterations and additions to the redraft, and noted any of significance.

> The time was now arrived when my professional pursuits were to be in

a great measure changed. Since the Duke of Bridgewater had (about the year 1760) introduced Canal navigation, it had made considerable progress in various parts of the Kingdom, and had been partially adopted in Shropshire. The advantages to be derived from this mode of conveyance, did not escape the attention of the enlightened *landowners* * *who aimed at accommodating their* rich and thriving *county with* Canal navigation, so as to unite the Rivers Severn, Dee, and Mersey; for which purpose, they *caused the levels to be ascertained, and a plan*† formed; – and so *eager* at that time *were the public* for Canal speculations, that, at the first general meeting, four times the estimated expense was, without hesitation, subscribed; and an Act of Parliament was obtained in 1793.

When the *affair*‡ was so far arranged in 1793 as to justify the commencement of practical operations, the committee *of management*, composed chiefly of *county* magistrates, *having*, at the quarter sessions and other public meetings, observed *that* the county works were conducted *to their satisfaction*, were pleased to propose my *undertaking the conduct of*§ this extensive and complicated *work; and feeling in myself* a stronger disposition for executing works of importance and magnitude, than for *the details* of house architecture, I did not hesitate to accept their offer, and from that time directed my attention *solely* to Civil Engineering. *As most of the difficulties which occur in Canal making must be overcome by means of masonry and carpentry, my previous occupations had so far given me confidence; and in regard* to earth work, I had the advantage of consulting Mr William Jessop, an experienced engineer, on whose advice I never failed to set a proper value.¶

Telford goes on to describe the canal as existing when he wrote, though he makes no mention of the major change from the old line as planned from Wrexham to Ruabon to the later one by way of the old Chester Canal, a change that left Pontcysyllte aqueduct on a water-supply and industrial branch instead of the main line.

He moves to locks. The printed text reads:

The locks upon this canal are generally of the usual form (See Plate 11), excepting as to their gates; for having experienced that even those made of the best English oak in a few years are subject to decay, and that the

---

* 'proprietors' in the re-draft.

† One notes that there is still no mention of Jessop, who was responsible for the levels and subsequent plan.

‡ In the re-draft originally 'Company's business'; 'Company's' has then been deleted.

§ Telford's wording in the re-draft was originally (and correctly) 'acting as General Agent to'. The much stronger, and incorrect, 'undertaking the conduct of', appears to be Rickman's.

¶ One notices that experience in iron work is not mentioned, and that Jessop has become 'an experienced engineer', instead of 'an experienced Canal engineer'.

renewal of them obstructs the navigation, considering also that iron abounded in Shropshire, and was more durable than timber alternately wet and dry, the uprights and ribs of the large lock-gates have for several years past been constructed with that material. For locks of 14 feet beam, the lower gates (being in two leaves) are cast heads and heels and ribs in separate pieces, with flanches* and, being fastened together with nuts and screws, are sheeted with wooden planking . . . . Some of these gates have been in use upwards of 20 years, and show no symptoms of decay. The application of cast-iron has in one instance on this canal been carried to a still greater extent, nearly opposite to Beeston Castle, in Cheshire; where a couple of locks, together rising 17 feet, having been built upon a stratum of quicksand, were repeatedly undermined, which suggested the idea of constructing the entire locks of cast-iron; and this extraordinary application of a new material has been successfully accomplished, and answers the purpose (see Plate 11). This mode, although expensive in the first instance, may in similar situations be practised with advantage.

One phrase needs to be noted, 'this extraordinary application of a new material'. It is not Telford's for it does not occur in the first version, and in the second is inserted in Rickman's handwriting. If it refers only to locks made entirely of cast-iron, like those at Beeston, it is probably correct, though irrelevant, for the Beeston locks date from 1827, long after our period. Even if it refers to iron used for lock-gates and other lock purposes, it still does not apply to our period. Iron for lock-gates on the Ellesmere Canal was not introduced until about 1819[4]. Cast-iron gates were introduced much earlier on the Caledonian Canal, Telford himself having written in 1813; '. . . delays experienced in attempting to procure Oak Timber of the requisite shape, dimensions and quality, have led Mr Jessop and myself to adopt Cast-Iron . . .'[5] and before that on a dock in Scotland's Carron River[6]. Rickman here assumes Telford's text refers to a much earlier period of the Ellesmere's history than it does; nevertheless its insertion conditions the reader's mind to the book's treatment of the aqueducts.

Later, Telford writes in his first draft of canal structures:

In Plate   I have shown the sort of Bridges, Stop Gates, Lett-offs, etc, which are employed; these do not differ from what are on other Canals . . .

The same wording appears as the basis of the second draft. It was,

* A footnote explains the meaning of the word.

67

however, then altered on the draft, but more radically after it. Here is the printed text:

> I have given specimens of the lock gates, canal bridges, stop-gates and tunnel, for the information of the inexperienced, not that they differ from those on other canals, unless in a kind of stop-gate, which being drawn across the canal, may be shut in whatever direction the water is running. (See Plate 12)

We may note that the words 'lock gates' do not appear in the manuscript – correctly, for Jessop's drawings for them survive. The words must have been added by Rickman, the word 'tunnel' was also added after the re-draft; as Telford at that time had had little experience of the difficult art of canal tunnelling, and Jessop indeed had, we can assume the drawing to be based on Jessop's work. Here we have Rickman, who seems to have had no personal knowledge of the Ellesmere Canal, inserting incorrect statements into Telford's text.

Then follows the section on aqueducts (see my Chapter 5), and then the inscription from an iron plate upon one of Pontcysyllte's piers which Telford had quoted in the documentation described in Chapter 3. The attributions are slightly altered, mainly to show Telford's membership of the Royal Society of London and Edinburgh:

> THOMAS TELFORD, F.R.S.L. & E. was Engineer.
> MATTHEW DAVIDSON was Superintendent of the Work.
> JOHN SIMPSON and JOHN WILSON executed the Masonry.
> WILLIAM HAZLEDINE executed the Iron Work.
> WILLIAM DAVIES made the Earthen Embankment.

There follows some geographical and tonnage information, and finally the Conclusion signed by the Earl of Bridgewater that was reproduced in Chapter 3. But with one tiny but significant alteration. Here it is, as printed in the *Life*:

> Having now detailed the particulars relative to the Canal, and the circumstances of the concern, the Committee, in concluding their report, think it but justice due to Mr. Telford to state, that the works have been planned with great skill and science, and executed with much economy and stability, doing him, as well as those employed by him, infinite credit.
>
> (signed) BRIDGEWATER.

and now requoted from the original:

HAVING now detailed the particulars relative to the Canal, and the circumstances of the concern, the Committee, in concluding this Report, thinks it a justice due to Mr. Telford, to state, that the works have been planned with great skill and science, and executed with much œconomy, precision, and stability, doing him, as well as those employed, infinite credit.

BRIDGEWATER
Chairman.

The last few words, originally 'doing him, as well as those employed, infinite credit' have been altered to 'doing him, as well as those employed by him, infinite credit'.

Those two added words 'by him' embody Telford's claim, at the end of his life, to have been sole engineer of the Ellesmere Canal. But we now have the two manuscript originals. The first, by Telford above, does not contain 'by him'; the second in Telford's writing again does not, but it has been amended, in Rickman's unmistakable hand, by adding 'by him'. Why did this highly respectable former civil servant deliberately alter a published printed text before reprinting it, in order to make it more favourable to the Telford of twenty-five years earlier?

What have the principal biographers said? First comes Samuel Hughes, himself an engineer, in his 'Memoir of William Jessop' published in 1844, six years after the *Life*. Hughes knew people who had worked with Jessop; yet Telford's *Life* had been published, with no suggestion that it was not entirely Telford's own. Hughes' account of the Ellesmere Canal attempts to straddle what he himself knew to be true with what the text of the *Life* said.

The Act for this canal was passed in the year 1793, and Mr. Jessop, who, in conjunction with Mr. Dadford, had obtained the Act, was appointed principal engineer. Mr. Telford, who was then county surveyor of Salop, in which capacity he had become favourably known to many of the leading proprietors in that county, was offered the appointment of acting engineer, which he accepted. This is the statement made in his life by Mr. Telford himself, and it is clearly borne out by a fact which will presently be adverted to, notwithstanding some assertions which have been made, to the effect that Telford was merely the agent or superintendent of the Canal Company, and not an engineer at all at that time. If this statement has been made to detract from Telford's merit, with respect to the great aqueducts and other works on this canal, and to swell in a corresponding degree the credit of Jessop, the attempt appears

CONCLUSION.

    HAVING now detailed the particulars relative to the Canal, and the circumstances of the concern, the Committee, in concluding this Report, thinks it a justice due to Mr. Telford, to state, that the works have been planned with great skill and science, and executed with much œconomy, precision, and stability, doing him, as well as those employed, infinite credit.

BRIDGEWATER,
Chairman.

(b) *[handwritten manuscript]*

"Having now detailed the particulars relative to the Canal, and the
"circumstances of the concern, the Committee, in concluding their Report;
"think it ~~but~~ justice due to Mr. Telford to state, that the Works have
"been planned with great skill and science, and executed
"with much œconomy and stability, doing him as well as those
    _{by him}
"employed infinite credit.

        (Signed) Bridgewater

(c)   " *Having now detailed the particulars relative to the Canal, and the circumstances of the concern, the Committee, in concluding their report, think it but justice due to Mr. Telford to state, that the works have been planned with great skill and science, and executed with much economy and stability, doing him, as well as those employed by him, infinite credit.*

(signed)   *BRIDGEWATER."*

Fig 10: (a) Reproduces the original statement by the Earl of Bridgewater in the 1805 documents; (b) The original manuscript of Telford's second version, as amended by John Rickman, in whose handwriting are the added words 'by him'; (c) The finished text as printed in Life of Thomas Telford, civil engineer, *written by himself...*

quite gratuitous and unnecessary; for Telford acknowledges candidly enough the advantage he derived from consulting Mr. Jessop, on whose advice, in his own words, he 'never failed to set a proper value.'

The inscription on the aqueduct of Pont-y-cysylte clearly states, that Thomas Telford, F.R.S.L. & E., was engineer of the work; and it is remarkable that no other engineer is mentioned. Telford's testimonial from the Committee of the Ellesmere Canal Company, printed and circulated at their general meeting in 1805, affords also conclusive evidence, that whoever else was employed as engineer, he at least was one, for it states, 'that the works have been planned with great skill and science, and executed with much economy and ability, doing him, (Mr. Telford,) as well as those employed by him, infinite credit.'

(Signed) 'BRIDGEWATER.'

In these paragraphs he asserts, correctly, that Jessop had been appointed principal engineer. In going on he reveals to us that Jessop's friends had been roused by the *Life* to assert that Telford was the agent or superintendent and not an engineer at all. My Chapter 2 sets out what I conceive to be the correct position. Hughes, however, has been misled by the *Life*'s implication that Telford's name had been inscribed on the aqueduct itself, and again by not knowing (how could he?) that Rickman had improved the Earl of Bridgewater's original printed encomium by adding 'by him' to the Earl's last sentence. So within a few years of publication did the *Life* begin to slant history.

Later, having got himself confused over the Longdon aqueduct, Hughes gets himself almost back on the rails in his last two paragraphs about Pontcysyllte.

At the same time, although it appears clear that Mr Telford proposed the use of cast iron to Mr Jessop, the latter has all the credit of designing the vast height and proportions of these great aqueducts, which far exceeded any thing that had ever before been attempted. He being the principal engineer, the levels and general features were settled by him, and to him is due the bold and successful attempt of carrying the canal at this great height, instead of locking up and down into the valley, at so great an expense of time and water that the prospects of the whole concern would have been vitiated for many years.

It was scarcely to be expected that Mr Jessop, from his position as chief engineer, could minutely adjust all the details of even large works like these; and it is at least highly indicative of his honourable and liberal mind, that he acquiesced at once in the judicious views of his acting engineer, to whom the more immediate charge of executing the work was committed.

Here now is Samuel Smiles, the first great populariser of engineering biography, whose book, *Lives of the engineers, with an account of their principal works ...* first published in 1861–2, was for long widely read and accepted:

> Although Mr Pulteney's influence had no doubt assisted Telford in obtaining the appointment of surveyor, it had nothing to do with the unsolicited invitation which now emanated from the county gentlemen. Telford was not even a candidate for the engineership, and had not dreamt of offering himself, so that the proposal came upon him entirely by surprise. Though he admitted he had self-confidence, he frankly confessed that he had not a sufficient amount of it to justify him in aspiring to the office of engineer to one of the most important undertakings of the day. The following is his own account of the circumstance:
>
>> My literary project is at present at a stand, and maybe retarded for some time to come, as I was last Monday appointed sole agent, architect, and engineer to the canal which is projected to join the Mersey, the Dee, and the Severn. It is the greatest work, I believe, now in hand in this kingdom, and will not be completed for many years to come. You will be surprised that I have not mentioned this to you before; but the fact is that I had no idea of any such appointment until an application was made to me by some of the leading gentlemen, and I was appointed, though many others had made much interest for the place. This will be a great and laborious undertaking, but the line which it opens is vast and noble; and coming as the appointment does in this honourable way, I thought it too great an opportunity to be neglected, especially as I have stipulated for, and been allowed, the privilege of carrying on my architectural profession. The work will require great labour and exertions, but it is worthy of them all.★
>
> Telford's appointment was duly confirmed by the next general meeting of the shareholders of the Ellesmere Canal. An attempt was made to get up a party against him, but it failed.
>
>> I am fortunate, in being on good terms with most of the leading men, both of property and abilities; and on this occasion I had the decided support of the great John Wilkinson, king of the ironmasters, himself a host. I travelled in his carriage to the meeting, and found him much disposed to be friendly.†
>
> The salary at which Telford was engaged was 500l. a year, out of

---

★ This quotation has been telescoped by Smiles from the original letter.
† Letter to Andrew Little, 29 September 1793. The quotation is shortened from the original.

which he had to pay one clerk and one confidential foreman, besides defraying his own travelling expenses.

... He now looked forward with anxiety to the commencement of the canal, the execution of which would necessarily call for great exertion on his part, as well as unremitting attention and industry;

for, said he, besides the actual labour which necessarily attends so extensive a public work, there are contentions, jealousies, and prejudices, stationed like gloomy sentinels from one extremity of the line to the other. But, as I have heard my mother say that an honest man might look the Devil in the face without being afraid, so we must just trudge along in the old way.*

... The Act authorising the construction of the canal was obtained in 1793, and Telford commenced operations very shortly after his appointment in October of the same year. His first business was to go carefully over the whole of the proposed line, and make a careful working survey, settling the levels of the different lengths, and the position of the locks, embankments, cuttings and aqueducts. In all matters of masonry work he felt himself master of the necessary details; but having had comparatively small experience of earthwork, and none of canal-making, he determined to take the advice of Mr William Jessop on that part of the subject; and he cordially acknowledges the obligations he was under to that eminent engineer for the kind assistance which he received from him on many occasions.

When writing of cast iron, Smiles says (p.361):

The uses of cast iron in canal construction became more obvious with every year's successive experience; and Telford was accustomed to introduce it in many cases where formerly only timber or stone had been employed. On the Ellesmere, and afterwards on the Caledonian Canal, he introduced cast iron lock-gates, which were found to answer admirably, being more durable than timber, and not liable like it to shrink and expand with alternate dryness and wet. The turnbridges which he introduced upon his canals, instead of the old drawbridges, were also of cast iron; and in some cases even the locks themselves were of the same material. Thus, on a part of the Ellesmere Canal opposite Beeston Castle, in Cheshire, where a couple of locks, together rising 17 feet, having been built on a stratum of quicksand, were repeatedly undermined, the idea of constructing the entire locks of cast iron was suggested; and this extraordinary application of the new material was successfully accomplished, with entirely satisfactory results.

But Telford's principal application of cast iron was in the construction of road bridges, in which he proved himself a master. His experi-

---

* Letter to Andrew Little, 3 November 1793.

ence of these structures had now become very extensive. During the time that he held the office of surveyor to the country of Salop, he erected no fewer than forty-two, five of which were of iron. Indeed, his success in iron bridge-building so much emboldened him, that in 1801 he submitted an iron bridge design for a new London Bridge.

We see here that Smiles has followed the Little letters and, in its reference to Jessop, the printed *Life*. Sir Alexander Gibb does better. Gibb was himself an engineer, one whose great-grandfather had worked for Telford. His was the first well-researched (given the limitations of his time) biography of Telford[7].

In 1790 the rage was all for canals ... Shropshire and Gloucestershire and the Welsh border offered an attractive field for development. A rich agricultural area, it contained too, coal and iron. Obviously among the more promising projects of the time, therefore, was a canal such as the Ellesmere Canal, designed to connect the Severn with the Mersey by way of Shrewsbury and the River Dee. Its first known advocate was one Charles Turner, described as architect and civil engineer, who published his views in a pamphlet that appeared in 1791 at Chester. As ultimately elaborated, the canal was to include several branch connections or feeders to less important areas, making a total length of 103 miles. A public meeting in September 1791 followed the publication of Turner's views and secured enthusiastic support for the scheme. A Bill was promoted forthwith and the Act obtained early in 1793. The greatest optimism prevailed; the whole of the required capital was subscribed in eight hours. The position of Engineer was then advertised and a committee consisting of, among others, William Pulteney and John Wilkinson, the ironmaster, was appointed to consider applicants and make recommendations. Among the applications was one from 'Thomas Telford, Architect'; and later he was duly appointed General Agent, Surveyor, Engineer, Architect and Overlooker to the Ellesmere Canal, on a salary of £500 a year, out of which he was to keep his own clerk and confidential foreman, and to meet his own expenses. He had also to find a surety in £5,000.

'Last Monday', wrote Telford to Little, 'I was appointed Sole Agent, Architect and Engineer to the Canal which is to join the Mersey and Dee and the Severn. It is the greatest work I believe, that is now in hand, in this kingdom, and will not be completed for many years to come. You will be surprised that I have not mentioned this to you before, but the fact is that I had no idea of any such thing untill an application was made to me from some of the leading Gentlemen, and I was appointed at their meeting, tho many others had made much interest for the place. I cannot be said to be confirmed untill after the general assembly of the

74

Proprietors which is to be held on 31 Octr. tho' 'tis not likely that that meeting will do away with the act of a numerous Committee of the leading Men. This is a great and laborious undertaking but the line which it opens is vast and noble, and coming in this honourable way I thought it too great an opportunity to be neglected. Mr. Pulteney approves much of it, as do all my friends. it will require great exertions but it is worthy of them all, there is a very great Aqueduct over the Dee, besides Bridges over several Rivers, which cross the Line of March.'

He was a little premature in reporting his appointment . . . it was not until the 3rd November, 1793, that it was finally settled. He reported the same day to Little –

'I duly received yours of the 6th Oct. but agreeable to your request I deferred answering it untill I could let you know the determination of the general meeting of the Ellesmere Canal Navigation, which was held last Wednesday. They have confirmed my appointment as general Agent. I have reserved the right to carry on such of my architectural business as does not require my personal attendance, so that I shall retain all I wish for of that, which are the Public Buildings and Houses of importance. The other parts of our business are better to be without: they give a great deal of unpleasant labour for very little profit in short they are like the calls of a Country Surgeon. These I shall give up without reluctance, except what relates to Mr Pulteney and Lady Bath and I have the pleasure to say that they are not disposed to quit me. You will not be surprised that altho this employment was offered to me, that there should be many who looked forward to it with anxious eyes and that they had endeavoured to raise a party at the general meeting, but we were too powerful for opposition. I am fortunate in being on good terms with most of the leading men whether of property or abilities and on this occasion I had the decided support of the great John Wilkinson, king of the Iron Masters, who is in himself an host. I travelled in his Carriage to the Meeting and found him much disposed to be friendly.'

At the same time William Jessop was appointed what would now be called consulting engineer to the project; and so began a connection between Telford and Jessop that lasted a quarter of a century to the pleasure and advantage of both. Telford had a profound trust in Jessop's experience and judgment, and up to his death in 1814 sought to bring him into any work with which he was connected requiring special engineering skill, particularly in regard to water or harbour work. Jessop was of a retiring nature, and is consequently among those who have passed almost unchronicled. But he played an important part in the development of civil engineering; he was connected with many of the outstanding works of his day and his reputation for soundness and common sense stood high. Matthew Davidson was almost as thrilled by Telford's appointment as was Telford himself. 'Davidson is canal mad,' wrote Telford, 'and there will now be occasion for all his exertions, for besides the real labour that attends such a great public work, Contentions, jealousies and prejudices are stationed like gloomy sentinels from one extremity of the Line to the other. But as I have heard my mother say, that an honest man might look the Devil in the face without being afraid, we must trudge on in the old way.'

This account[8] is interesting, for Gibb has gone wider for his facts. He takes the project back to 1791 by mentioning Turner's pamphlet (though the author was Joseph not Charles), and the public meeting of (15th) September of that year. He is, however, unaware that Jessop's name, recommended by Smeaton to make a survey, was accepted soon afterwards, on 7 November. That he had access either to the minute book or to a record of the September meeting is suggested by his moving straight on to his paragraph about Jessop.

Gibb on Jessop is generous, but upon wrong premises, for he misunderstands the roles of the two men. Jessop, as we have seen, was engaged in 1791, and had since then twice surveyed the line, and taken the Bill through Parliament. His title was Principal Engineer, and is so given in the Committee's minute appointing Telford, among other titles, 'engineer'.

Later Gibb quotes one surviving letter from Jessop to Telford without realising that the wording in itself suggested a working relationship of principal and resident engineer much more than one of engineer and consultant – as in its beginning:

'In looking forward to the time when we shall be laying the Iron Trough on the Piers . . . .'.

Surely that 'we' is enlightening? The same is true a year later when the design of Chirk aqueduct was being altered. Telford writes to Matthew Davidson:

I have seen Mr Jessop as to the Aqueduct at Chirk, and he agrees as to the general principle of the adopting Brick or Rubble Arches instead of an Iron Trough . . . . Mr Jessop wishes you to consider whether inverted Brick Arches laid upon Flannel would not answer and be much cheaper than the stone Bottom . . . .

Because Gibb misunderstands the relationship, he is wildly mistaken in talking of Telford bringing Jessop into any work. Jessop was always the senior. One must somewhat wryly observe that the

76

fact that Jessop is 'among those who have passed almost unchronicled' is partly – as this book maintains – Telford's and Rickman's own responsibility.

In our own times, L.T.C. Rolt is another widely-read populariser of engineering biography. When he came to write his *Thomas Telford* in 1958 he did indeed have access to the minute books, and his account of the canal's origin is straightforward. Indeed he asks whether it is not in fact the case that 'Telford was in the position of a resident engineer working under Jessop', and replies to himself that 'it was Telford who originated the designs and submitted them to Jessop for his approval'. 'So', he goes on, 'it is safe to say that the major share of the credit for the great works on the Ellesmere Canal is due to Telford, although it is quite true that inadequate tribute has been paid in the past to that modest* man, William Jessop'. But here Rolt is deceiving himself. First, we know, though Rolt did not, that Jessop did the Ellesmere's lock drawings. Second, we know that the designing of Pontcysyllte took place in two stages; a general decision to build an aqueduct carrying an iron trough upon masonry piers, and, several years later, the detailed design work. As to the first general decision, we have no facts, only surmises; as to the detailed work, done long after the period of which Rolt is writing, it was almost certainly done by Telford and the ironmaster William Hazledine working together.

But in between we do know that Jessop, in a report of 14 July 1795, that Rolt does not quote, had recommended an iron trough aqueduct at the full height of 125ft, and that the managing committee had on 10 August agreed in these words: 'It is ordered that the recommendation of Mr Jessop in that respect shall be adopted and the General Surveyor and Agent to the Company (note the word 'Engineer' is not used) is hereby directed to proceed in the same works conformably thereto.' Here, surely, is Rolt's answer.

Then, nearly a century and a half after publication of the *Life*, we reach accuracy at last. Neil Cossons, in his 'Foreword' to the printed *Proceedings* of a seminar held in 1979[9] describes Telford as General Agent as 'Working under William Jessop' and a dominant personality 'second only to Jessop', and Derrick Beckett, in *Telford's Britain*[10] writes

---

* The word 'modest' derives, one would think, from Gibb.

As we have seen, Jessop was appointed engineer to the canal company in 1791, but it was not until September 1793 that Telford was appointed 'General Agent, Surveyor, Engineer, Architect and Overlooker of the Works to make Reports to superintend the cutting forming and making the Canal and taking up and seeing the due observance of the levels thereof to make the Drawings and to submit such Drawings to the Consideration and Correction of Mr William Jessop . . . His engagement to extend to all Architecture and Engineering Business to the Drawing forming and directing the making of Bridges, Aqueducts Tunnels Locks Buildings Reservoirs Wharfs and other works' (C. Hadfield and A. W. Skempton).★

This is a most revealing job description and indicates Telford's position in relation to Jessop, who held overall responsibility for the works.

It has been a long journey.

★ Professor Skempton and I are of course quoting *verbatim* from the minute book.

Chapter 5

Centres of the Myth: Longdon, Pontcysyllte and Chirk Aqueducts

No-one, I suppose, has seen Pontcysyllte aqueduct, 126ft above the Dee, 1007ft long, without being astonished by what may well be the finest monument given us by the Industrial Revolution. Its genesis and construction have been especially interesting to me since that day in 1954 when for the first time I saw it, indeed walked across it in a high wind, in company with a canal engineer. Fourteen years or so later, I took a boat across and back.

I. Pont-y-Cafnau and Longdon aqueducts

Before Pontcysyllte came Longdon, and before Longdon, Pont-y-Cafnau. Let us first consider these.

Pont-y-Cafnau (Bridge of Troughs) in Glamorganshire had been built 'between January and June 1793 to carry an edge-railway and a water channel taking limestone and water power respectively to the Cyfarthfa ironworks'[1]. An 'A' frame bridge supported a tramroad, and suspended beneath the track platform was an iron trough aqueduct. It was built by Watkin George, chief engineer of Cyfarthfa ironworks, and a former carpenter. He 'seems to have adapted a king-post roof truss design'.[2]

In Reynolds' 'Sketchbook' in the Science Museum Library is a sketch of this 'A' frame bridge. It appears with others on p. 78 which refer to 'Lord D'. Philip Cohen, in a postscript to an article upon 'Origins of the Pontcysyllte Aqueduct'[3], referring to an article on the 'Sketchbook' by H. W. Dickinson[4], writes:

> In his discussion of the other sketches on page 78, Dickinson suggested that 'Lord D', was Lord Dundonald, the proprietor of extensive tar distillation works at Calcutts and Benthall, in the Ironbridge Gorge. His tar and coke kilns were operated as an integral part of adjacent iron works, and it is quite natural that he should visit the works at Cyfarthfa. He was known to be on friendly terms with William Reynolds, and

79

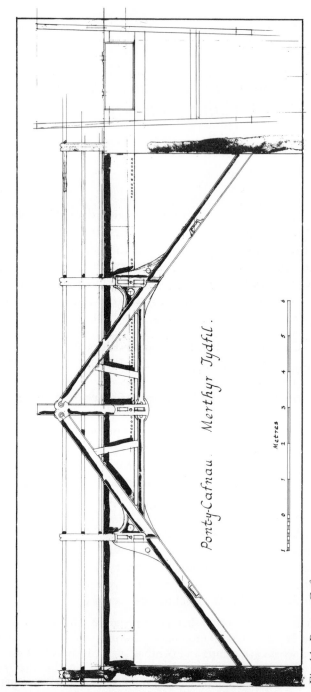

Fig 11: Pont-y-Cafnau.

these drawings presumably depict scenes visited by Dundonald that were of interest to Reynolds. One possibility is that Dundonald knew of Reynolds' interest in iron aqueducts, and therefore took details of this one at Cyfarthfa. On his return to Shropshire in April 1794, he would then describe the structure to Reynolds, and hence the drawing appears in the Sketchbook.

Therefore Reynolds is likely to have learned of this iron trough aqueduct and its supporting structures soon after April 1794, the date of the other structures on the same page of drawings that Lord Dundonald presumably then gave him.[5]

The Shrewsbury Canal, like the Ellesmere, had been authorised in 1793 to run from that city to join the small existing Wombridge Canal, extension of the older Donnington Wood Canal, early components of the chain of small canals that was to serve the Coalbrookdale–Horsehay–Lilleshall ironworks area. The Wombridge being for 8-ton tub-boats, the Shrewsbury was at first intended to be the same. William and Richard Reynolds were active in its promotion, as were John Wilkinson and those concerned with the Donnington Wood Canal, the Marquess of Stafford, and John and Thomas Gilbert; all were in the iron business.

Josiah Clowes, an experienced second-rank man, was appointed engineer under William Reynolds. Among the canal works, he had

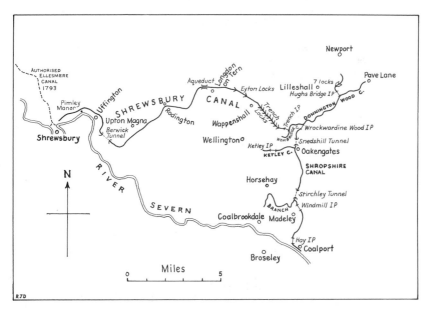

Fig 12: The Shrewsbury Canal and its connections.

81

begun a masonry aqueduct over the little river Tern at Longdon. Then in early 1795 Clowes died, and the disastrous and widespread floods of 10–12 February washed away the part-built aqueduct along with much else.

William Reynolds and those associated with him in what we can consider as the Ketley ironworks interest on the canal committee were its leaders. At a meeting on 23 February 1795 Telford, by now General Agent under William Jessop on the Ellesmere Canal, was called in, probably by Reynolds, to examine flood damage at the canal's three aqueduct sites, including Longdon. At another meeting on 28 February he was told to make a plan and estimate of alterations and additions to Longdon, and at the same meeting was appointed engineer in Clowes' place.

Two weeks later, on 14 March, with the Reverend John Rocke in the chair, and William Reynolds and Thomas Eyton, associated with him, among others round the table, the canal committee discussed a replacement for the aqueduct, and: 'Ordered that an Iron Aqueduct be erected at Longdon (agreeable to a plan to be approved by Mr Telford) by Messrs William Reynolds & Company' at a cost not to exceed £2000. So says the minute book, where we may note the word 'approved'. The minute continues after 'Company', 'Messrs Wm Reynolds & Company agreeing to compleat the said Aqueduct on or before the 14th September next and to uphold the same for the space of 5 Years'. Telford was to remove the soil near the present aqueduct and to 'make preparations for the erection of the Iron Aqueduct to be erected there'.

As Neil Cossons and Barrie Trinder, followed by the late J. G. James, pointed out[6], there was little interest in iron bridges or aqueducts until the great floods of early 1795. Large numbers of bridges all over the country were then destroyed, Buildwas among them, but the iron bridge at Coalbrookdale survived, a fact that was widely commented on. Commonsense suggests that, to enable William Reynolds at the 14 March meeting to agree to design, make and erect the aqueduct in six months, he must have started planning a new one as soon as he had heard that Clowes' partly-built masonry structure had been destroyed, for the commercial need to finish the canal was considerable. We can assume, therefore, that he based himself on Pont-y-Cafnau, and quickly worked out a design; hence the testing of iron bars that was being done at Ketley in March.

It suggests also that on 28 February the instruction to Telford to make 'a plan and estimate of alterations and additions to Longdon' refers to the damaged masonry structure, and meant that Reynolds was not yet ready with his iron aqueduct proposal. That came on 14 March, when the minute book records that its design was to be approved by Telford who was also to prepare the ground.

Yet here now is Telford, only four days after the meeting, writing on 18 March a letter to his boyhood friend Andrew Little that he can hardly have expected would ever be published:

> ... since I wrote you I have been appointed Engineer to another Canal called the Shrewsbury Canal ... I have just recommended an Iron Aqueduct for the most considerable work on the line, it is approved, and will be executed under my direction, upon a principle entirely new, and which I am endeavouring to establish with regard to the application of Iron.[7]

One gets the impression that Reynolds' proposal at the 14 March meeting for an iron aqueduct to be erected within six months had taken Telford by surprise. Having then thought it over, Telford disagreed. Thus he could at once have seen Reynolds to persuade him to allow more time for reconsideration of his original idea, because he himself had thought of a better one – and had succeeded.

Plymley's *General View of the Agriculture of Shropshire* was published in 1803. To it Telford contributed a substantial section on 'Canals', dated 13 November 1800 from Shrewsbury. Here is his account of the iron aqueduct's initiation:

> The idea of having this aqueduct made of cast-iron, was first suggested and recommended by THOMAS EYTON Esq.* then Chairman of the Committee; after due consideration it was approved of by the Committee, and the principles of construction, and the manner in which it should be executed, were referred to Mr. WILLIAM REYNOLDS and the Writer of this article, who, after several consultations, and forming and considering various plans, at last determined upon that which is represented by the annexed engravings, No. 3. The castings for the aqueduct were done at Ketley, and were removed to Long,† a distance of five miles, partly by land and partly by water-carriage.
>
> This aqueduct was proposed in consequence of the great floods which happened in the beginning of the year 1795, and it was fixed up complete in March, 1796.

---

* Eyton was a business associate of Reynolds. It may well be true that he first suggested the use of iron; if so, it is unlikely that this idea would have been put to Reynolds soon after the floods.

† Longdon is of course meant.

This paragraph was written by Telford less than six years after the events it describes had taken place, and published in three years more. Therefore most of those who had sat round the committee table in 1795 (notably William Reynolds, who died in 1803) would be still alive, and likely to read his account. We can therefore accept it as accurate.

If we now return to the Little letter, we can assume that 'recommended' must be read with 'upon a principle entirely new'. The idea of having an iron aqueduct must surely have been Reynolds'; 'executed under my direction' being interpreted, correctly, as implying 'under my direction as engineer'. But what was the 'principle entirely new', which so convinced Reynolds? On the one hand the ironmaster and mechanical engineer, accustomed to handling cast iron and timber, at that time indispensable for works like Reynolds' canal inclined planes or for plateways and their waggons, and well aware of the Coalbrookdale company's experience in iron bridge building[8]; on the other Telford, who earlier had been accustomed, as he himself later wrote, to 'the complicated details of House Architecture', and had then found that 'As . . . Canal Works consist chiefly of Masonry and Carpentry, my previous Avocations had qualified me to conduct them[9].

The authors of the article on Pont-y-Cafnau say of Longdon: 'The design . . . was basically of (mock-)timber inclined supports as observed on Pont-y-Cafnau supporting a flat (mock-)masonry arch composed of wedge-shaped sections (voussoirs). This was entirely appropriate as the deck was designed by Thomas Telford the mason, and the supports seem to be based on the earlier design by Watkin George the carpenter.' The supports for Longdon could therefore have been designed either by Reynolds or Telford; both had the experience. We may guess that the former had already designed some such supports, and was testing them, intending to erect the trough above them as a separate entity. Maybe Telford's contribution was to combine the two parts into one whole.

The arch was at that time the basic structural form, and early canal aqueducts were of that type. So at Longdon the lower part, consisting of cruciform-section struts, suggests the springing of the arch, the upper part arch voussoirs. If this were all in masonry the structure would collapse, although theoretically it would stand as all is in equilibrium. The fact that the plates are bolted together means that the 'arch' would survive intact no matter the buffeting it received during its working life. Perhaps this is how Telford looked

84

Fig 13: Longdon Aqueduct.

at it. Professor Schofield, in a letter to the author, writes that Longdon

> suggests that it was designed as a series of arches rather than a continuous beam, which might be the method employed today, or even a series of simple beams, which would be a satisfactory, but less economic design. Longdon nevertheless is, in a sense, a 'missing link' between arch and beam design. It represents a truly nice piece of engineering in both thought and execution.

We have some confirmation here from Sir David Brewster's review of Telford's *Life* in 1839[10]. Brewster is writing of Telford's first iron bridge, that at Buildwas above Coalbrookdale.

> The roadway rested upon a very flat arch, which was the segment of a very large circle; while this arch itself was sustained and strengthened by an outer arched rib on each side of the bridge, springing from a lower point than the flat arch, and rising as high as the top of the parapet railing; thus introducing the principle of timber trussing.

It was completed in 1796.

Let us hazard the opinion that Telford's new principle was derived from architecture; that cast iron, because of its strength and rigidity, should enable structures that formerly had had to be built of timber or masonry to be re-designed as a single whole, and so greatly improved?

The new design evolved jointly by Telford and Reynolds postponed the opening of Longdon aqueduct to a year after the meeting that authorised it. Its evolution must have taken about two months, i.e. to, say, mid-May. This dating is relevant when we come to consider the origins of Pontcysyllte.

Let us now see what Telford said of Longdon.

Here is the *Life*, in its printed version, as it begins his account of Pontcysyllte aqueduct:

> I had about that time carried the Shrewsbury Canal by a cast-iron trough at about 16 feet above the level of the ground; and finding this practicable, it occurred to me . . .[11]

This statement cannot be true. He was appointed engineer to the Shrewsbury Canal on 28 February 1795, and the iron aqueduct was agreed on 14 March. Jessop's report recommending iron troughs at Pontcysyllte and Chirk was presented to the Ellesmere Canal committee on 14 July (see p. 33). By that date fabrication of Longdon can hardly have begun, or its design been fully completed, for it was not opened until March 1796. Therefore Telford could not have found Longdon 'practicable' in any but a theoretical sense.

II. **Who conceived the idea of building Pontcysyllte and Chirk?**

The original western route of the canal was surveyed by Duncombe, who seems to have foreseen river crossings of the Dee and Ceiriog. But it was William Jessop who in his preliminary report on the canal in January 1792, drew attention to the fact that the route he proposed would require an aqueduct over the river Dee 970ft long and 126ft high. In fact, Pontcysyllte as built is 1007ft long and 126ft high. He then pointed out that it would be possible to reduce the cost by lowering it 24ft using three locks at each end, and pumping water back by a river-driven waterwheel. On 10 September his report was accepted, and on 30 April 1793 the authorising Act was passed, Jessop seeing it through the Lords committee.

On 19 August William Turner, one of the three engineering assistants then laying out the line, was told to prepare plans and estimates for the aqueducts at Pontcysyllte and Pontfaen (Chirk). No question of an iron aqueduct had then arisen – it was to be of masonry. On 23 September Telford was appointed General Agent, with Turner and Duncombe as assistants. On 17 January 1794, Turner's three-arched plan for Pontcysyllte at a lower level was adopted by the Committee, subject to any alterations Jessop might suggest. Telford was then to prepare a specification and working drawings. I have in Chapter 2 suggested that this might well have been at around the 100ft height.

Then on 21 March 1795 the committee 'Ordered that an accurate account shall be taken . . . of the stone raised and work done by James Varley the contractor for building the aqueduct at Pontcysylte', and also that he produce sureties for the performance of his contract. It may well have been now that a provisional decision was taken to reduce the height of the masonry aqueduct to 76ft, in order to speed up the work. I have suggested in Chapter 2 that it was one with which Jessop may not have concurred. Possibly Telford didn't either. The date was a week after an iron trough had been agreed for Longdon, and Telford's mind would probably have been full of it.

So, even before Longdon itself had been designed, he perhaps rushed off to sketch an idea of what Pontcysyllte might look like in iron before further discussions took place upon the masonry structure. He may have shown it to Jessop, but if so, why did it not find an honoured home in his own large collection of drawings, but instead in Reynolds' haphazard accumulation★[12] Did he perhaps first show it to Reynolds, who told him it was not practicable and that much more thought was needed? If so, he could have laid it aside until later when he gave it away. It is reproduced on p 89.

Let us examine it. It may not be Pontcysyllte at all, though it is so endorsed, not by Telford, on the back. The paper is contemporary, and the writing and style of drawing appear to be his. A major difficulty is the date of March 1794, written and signed by Telford, in a different ink to the drawing. The date seems most unlikely, if for no other reason that in his autobiography he would have said so; instead, he said he got the idea from Longdon. The '1794' date may be an accidental mistake, or it may have been written later to make an *ex post facto* claim to the genesis of Poncysyllte.

The drawing shows a most improbable structure, whose trough was to be supported entirely by trusses (two or even five according to interpretation), held on lattice piers. One's mind goes back to the timber-turned-into-iron struts of Pont-y-Cafnau. Some time ago, I showed the drawing to three engineering contacts, each separately, and without telling them what it represented. I then asked what material was intended for the piers: all three said: 'It looks like timber'. Was Telford excited by his idea, predicting that what might in improved form have stood in timber (for many high and long trestle railway viaducts were later to be built, for instance by Brunel), would stand when built in cast iron? And did Reynolds tell him he was wrong, for in iron it would probably have collapsed under its own weight and that of the trough?

The height shown (about 100ft) is not the full height as built later, but approximates to that for which Varley had been cutting stone. It is too short at 310ft; the structure to be agreed in July was to be 350–410ft. The river bank profile is wrong. It makes use of the stone already cut only for the plinths. The canal water does not run under the towpath, as in the finished aqueduct, and therefore the structure is unbalanced. There is no towpath rail. Given the hurry in which he probably drew it, these points are unimportant. If the

★ The book's history is given in an article by H. W. Dickinson in Vol. II of *Trans Newcomen Soc*, pp132ff. It had been through many vicissitudes before it reached the Science Museum's Library in about 1921. Their contemporary list describes the drawing as: 'Plan for a canal aqueduct with spans of 100 feet over a river. Signed 'March, 1794, Thos. Telford'. We may note that it is not here attributed to Pontcysyllte. Dickinson himself, exceptionally well-informed upon engineering history, wrote then: '. . . there is nothing in the volume of outstanding importance'.

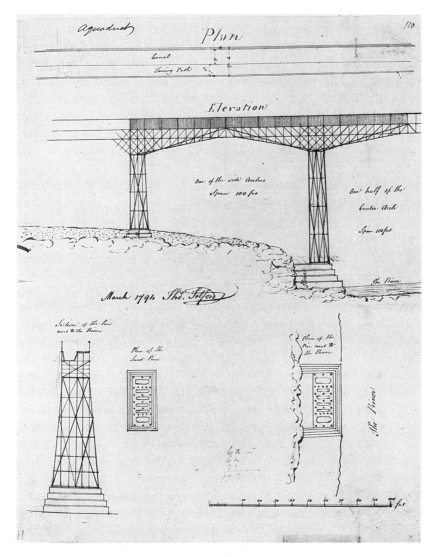

Fig 14: Drawing signed by Telford, dated March 1794 for an iron aqueduct.

origin I have suggested for the sketch is correct then 'March', though not 1794, could be right. If, however, it owes anything to Longdon except the idea of an iron trough on iron piers, 'March' cannot be correct either[13].

We move now from a dream structure to reality: Pontcysyllte and Chirk.

III. Who was responsible for Pontcysyllte's iron trough on masonry piers carried to the full height?

The period immediately after the great bridge destruction by floods of early 1795 was one of intense activity in the development of iron structures. The proposal by Reynolds and Telford for an iron aqueduct at Longdon was accepted in March 1795, to become an iron trough 186ft long in four spans supported at a height of 16ft above the river Tern on cast-iron pillars. Next month a contract was awarded to the Coalbrookdale Company for building an iron bridge over the Severn at Buildwas to Telford's design. On 11 June the Derby Canal Company authorised a cut across the Holmes, which implies that Benjamin Outram, the canal's engineer, had designed his single-span (44ft 6ins) iron trough aqueduct a little before this date. All three structures reached completion in 1796, as did the impressive 236ft span arch of the iron bridge at Sunderland which had been under construction by Thomas Wilson since 1793.

Meanwhile, in February 1795, the Peak Forest Canal Company, whose engineer was also Outram, had decided to build their great Marple aqueduct over the River Goyt in stone. Then, on 22 April, the American engineer Robert Fulton, one of their contractors, proposed 'substituting Cast Iron instead of Stone Arches for the Aqueduct'[14]. It was to have been 90ft high and 200ft long (so a contemporary newspaper reported, but probably a misprint for 300ft, for the present aqueduct is 309ft long, and it is difficult to see how another 100ft of embankment could have been built), presumably in three spans. No other details are known, but Fulton's intentions may have been as indicated by the engraving published on 1 March 1796 as Plate 13 in his *Treatise on the Improvement of Canal Navigation*, which shows an iron trough carried on iron arch ribs in a manner foreshadowing Pontcysyllte as built[15].

There is little doubt that each of the engineers in this tightly knit circle knew what the others were doing. Jessop, probably acquainted with Reynolds since 1788, was working with Outram and

90

Telford; Outram with Fulton, and Reynolds with Telford. Outram visited Reynolds soon after 23 April 1795 on Peak Forest Canal business[16]. Fulton greatly admired Reynolds' inclined planes, and put Jessop's name at the head of the engineers to whom he submitted some ideas on small canals in July 1795[17], while among the drawings later listed as in Telford's possession was one endorsed 'Details of an Iron Bridge by Robt Fulton 14 March 1795'.

The idea of building an iron trough aqueduct at Pontcysyllte may have come from several people. A reasonable hypothesis is that it was Telford's, derived by way of William Reynolds from Longdon, who in turn derived it from Pont-y-Cafnau. Equally reasonably, it could be credited to Jessop, whose Butterley partner Outram had completed his one-span aqueduct at the Holmes by February 1796. The important question is not who had the idea, but who first decided that it was practicable and could be built.

The answer must surely be William Jessop, for as principal engineer he was currently responsible for building the high masonry structure agreed upon, and also for holding down costs. Since he had proposed a reduced-height Pontcysyllte aqueduct at 102ft in 1792, much had happened. He had had an unfortunate experience with a masonry aqueduct on the Cromford Canal[18], and he had become a partner with Outram in the Butterley ironworks.

As regards the piers, however, commonsense had to come in. Varley had been cutting stone since about June of the previous year. Why use iron for supports, as at Longdon and in Telford's sketch? Why waste all this stone? Why not put an iron trough on stone piers and so use it? It would be typical of Jessop's characteristic care for shareholders' pockets in every job he did. Secondly, the stone piers could now be carried to full height, and it would make no difference to the trough, once the safety of the workmen had been assured. Thus the lock flights at each end of the current masonry aqueduct could be eliminated, and with them the problem, at that moment acute, of supplying the canal with water.

One now imagines meetings between Jessop and Telford, and certainly letters passing; if we had them, they would answer many of our questions about the aqueduct. There were also other canal matters, all leading up to the report dated from Shrewsbury (perhaps after a last conference with Telford) on 14 July 1795 in which iron troughs were proposed for Pontcysyllte and Chirk. One also presupposes, as Mr I. Davidson[19] suggests, that the evidence Jessop 'required of the feasibility of an iron trough, formed from flanged cast iron plates with screw bolts, and of the availability of sound castings at an economical price, would have been obtained immediately before writing the report, from an inspection of the plates recently cast by Reynolds for the Longdon Aqueduct. Possibly a trial erection of one span of the trough had been made by then'. He adds that 'Evidently Outram and Fulton were also convinced by what they saw at Reynolds' foundry at this time'.

At this time no 'design' can have existed, for, as we can see from Jessop's letter of 26 July, the essential decisions had yet to be made – how many piers, of what dimensions, with how many openings, what dimensions for the trough? And many more. In his report of 14 July he had suggested 7 'openings' of 50ft each (i.e. 350ft), the rest to be embankment, but when writing to Telford on the 26th he seems to have misremembered his own proposal, for he says '. . . it will be better . . . to have 8 openings of 52 feet . . . instead of 60 feet' i.e. 416ft instead of 480ft. In this same letter to Telford he determines pier dimensions – and we may note he does not ask Telford's opinion, but tells him: 'In the next place I would have the Piers 7 feet wide at the top instead of 6 feet, and make them about 2 feet more in the other dimensions.'

IV. Who was responsible for the components of Pontcysyllte?

Let me now return to Chapter 2, and summarise Pontcysyllte's chronology.

July/August	1795	Iron trough proposed and accepted. Work ordered to begin.
November	1795	Embankment begun.
February	1797	Price enquiries for ironwork and erection addressed to ironmasters. No result.
November	1799	Remaining mason's work advertised.
January	1800	Jessop recommended building remainder of piers hollow, and also design of abutments.
February	1800	Simpson's tender to complete the piers and abutments accepted. Trough and ironwork probably designed.

92

March	1802	Hazledine's tender for executing and erecting the ironwork accepted.
	1802–1805	Main period of construction.
November	1805	Opening.

I can now attempt to tabulate, from the evidence we have examined, the known and likely responsibilities for Pontcysyllte aqueduct.

(a) *Decision* to build at full height, Jessop.

(b) *The iron trough. Idea,* either Telford, by way of William Reynolds, and arising out of the choice of iron for Pont-y-Cafnau and Longdon aqueducts; or Jessop, by way of Outram; *responsibility for decision to recommend for committee's approval,* Jessop; *design,* probably Telford and Hazledine (or his foreman, Stuttle) in collaboration; *execution,* Hazledine; *final approval,* Jessop.

(c) *Piers. Choice of stone,* Jessop, suggested by amount already cut; *design,* probably Jessop, given the surviving evidence, but with Telford's likely help; *execution,* Telford and Simpson.

(d) *Abutments,* Jessop; *execution,* Telford and Simpson.

(e) *Embankment,* Jessop; *execution,* Telford and Davies.

(f) *Decision to extend the trough, increase the number of piers, and reduce the embankment length.* Probably Telford after discussion with Jessop.

(g) *Overall engineering responsibility,* Jessop, from inception to opening; *execution,* Telford with Matthew Davidson as general superintendent.

In other words, the creation of the aqueduct followed the normal pattern; overall responsibility for design and suitability to purpose was Jessop's as principal engineer; overall responsibility for execution (other than of the trough) was Telford's as resident, with specialists beneath him; overall responsibility for casting and erecting the trough, Hazledine. Jessop's role, if any, in the design of the trough is unknown (as is Telford's), but commonsense suggests that his approval, both as principal engineer and ironmaster in his own right, was obtained before proceeding to execution. To sum up, one asks oneself who would have been held finally responsible had Pontcysyllte failed, partially or wholly, at any time up to and including its opening day? Surely the answer can only be Jessop.

We have an independent contemporary witness to Jessop's overall responsibility. John Farey, author of the article 'Canal' in Rees' *Cyclopaedia*, wrote, probably in 1805:

> ... A most stupendous work of this kind [aqueducts] has been under-taken by Mr Jessop, on the Ellesmere canal, and is now nearly or quite completed, for crossing the Dee river at Pontcysyltee ... where nine-teen massive conical pillars of stone, at fifty-two feet from each other ... support between the top of every pair, a number of elliptical cast-iron ribs, which by means of uprights and horizontal bars, support a cast-iron aqueduct about 329 yards long ... composed of massive sheets of cast-iron ...

Farey's details are wrong, but his conclusion is clear.

V. **Who was responsible for Chirk Aqueduct?**

In his report of 14 July 1795 Jessop had recommended that this too should be of iron, though here the committee on 10 August had not given formal endorsement, but only authorised further examination. Tenders must have been quickly sought, for on 20 January 1796 the committee minuted that 'John Simpson and William Hazledine of Salop Builders and William Davies of Chirk ... Victualler who have delivered the most reasonable proposal for executing the aqueduct over the River Ceiriog ...' should be appointed contractors, the work to be finished by 1 October 1798.

Yet on 11 February Telford writes to Davidson:

> Mr Jessop is in London but we have hitherto been so busy that I have not had time to consult him as to the Chirk Aqueduct, but I shall in a day or two and if you think of any other matter that requires his advise be so good as write me from time to time and every day if necessary when he and I have such favourable opportunity of consulting together.

On 15 February 1796 he writes from London again to Davidson:

> I have seen Mr. Jessop as to the Aqueduct at Chirk, and he agrees as to the general principle of the adopting Brick or Rubble Arches instead of an Iron Trough, only that he thinks that the Piers should be set out so as to allow 6 feet instead of 5 feet on each side of the Canal★ – the distance between the Piers to be 45 feet, or it would not increase the expense very much, say 40 feet as John Simpson thinks that 45 is a great deal for Brick

★ Jessop was here probably thinking of his disastrous experience with the Derwent aqueduct on the Cromford Canal, where the spandrels bulged and collapsed because they were so high and much too slender to withstand the earth pressures behind them. He should have made them very much thicker. Professor Schofield makes the same point when he writes to me: '... was not the Chirk design influenced by the knowledge resulting from the Derwent failure? I should be surprised if it was not.'

Arches, but we should know the probable difference of expense and Mr. Jessop wishes you to consider whether inverted Brick Arches laid upon Flannel would not answer and be much cheaper than the stone bottom, but since I left Mr. Jessop I have been recollecting that in the case of Brick Arches, that the Spandrels must be brought up Solid.

This change of Plan must not be divulged at present as the proposed change must first be shown to Mr. Myddelton.

He wrote again on 9 March.

... I waited untill I had an opportunity of settling with Mr. Jessop respecting the Aqueduct, after considering it in every point of view, we find it by far the most adviseable *to adopt the Arches*. And I have sent down the Drawing to Shrewsbury that Mr. Simpson may give it to Mr. Lovet in order to get Mr Myddelton consent, who I should think would readily consent to the variation as it will in this way be an ornament to his beautiful Valley you should likewise wait upon Mr. Lovet and explain the Drawing – if Mr. Myddelton agrees to this last plan, you may give Mr. Simpson directions to proceed without delay.

I have noted Telford's relaxed relations with Jessop at this time. We have contemporary evidence for this. One Howell, who was then working with Davidson, had invented some sort of machine for boring wooden pipes. Telford was attracted to it as a business proposition, and on 9 March 1796, in the same letter as that quoted earlier, added to Davidson:

You may tell Mr. Howell I have not forgot the business of the Pipes – He will I presume have no objections if Mr. Jessop is taken in as a partner, I have only thought of this, this morning, but as he is going every where, and is every where known and respected, I think it would be a point of importance, if he will take a share, I shall have some conversation with him to-day and hear what he thinks of the matter in general, and if he is disposed to take an active part.

He wrote again on 31 March from London:

I have received yours of the 29th Mr. Jessop is not at present in London, but I shall state what occurs to me relative to the Chirk Aqueduct, and which I thought had been fully understood by all parties. Viz: – that it was to be 22 feet wide at the Top and to widen downwards at the rate of one Inch in a foot and length of Piers at the surface of the ground will of course be regulated by the distance from that surface to the top of the Aqueduct. The thickness of the piers to be 12 feet, and to be carried up parallel or nearly so. The Arches to be 45 feet in the Span, there could be little objection to making the Arches 40 feet in the Span only that I doubt

95

that 40 feet will be little for the River and the Meadow would be much cut away, by giving two Arches for the River to flow through, but this can best be determined on the Spot.

With regard to the offsets, as you will work with Rubble Stone, I should advise that the offsets be small and frequent, say 4 Inches at every foot in height. The number of offsets will be regulated by the depth you go for a foundation, there should be an offset at the height of about 3 feet above the Surface of the meadow, upon which there should be a Water Table* of Freestone but you will have no occasion for Freestone under the Surface of the ground.

As to the Foundations, it would be rash to give any positive direction, at this distance, Mr. Simpson and you are both good judges from long experience, and you are aware that no risque must be run, in such a Work, on account of foundations and that it is always best to go down to a good one if it is to be found at any reasonable depth.

Be sure to get Stornaway Lime for all the work which will be underground, and work the Lime fresh –

We need not be concerned with the reasons for this (apparently unminuted) change of mind by Telford, breaking back from iron to his old love of stone, though the difficulty of getting the iron to the site occurs at once. Our interest is in the wording of the letters. If Telford had been the originator of the iron trough proposals for Pontcysyllte and Chirk, would he so quickly have himself chosen to abandon iron at Chirk, especially as the committee had agreed to tender only a month before? One notices the relaxed tone of the letters, as if Telford had no personal, but only a practical, interest in the choice. As for Jessop, overwhelmed with work and with no special personal involvement in the iron aqueduct, he seems willing enough to have acquiesced in the change, merely making sure of practicalities that occurred to him.

The rest of the Chirk story is told in Chapter 2. Here responsibility is easy to allocate. Jessop took it for his original proposal of an iron trough. Thenceforward the moving spirit was Telford, who at each relevant stage sought Jessop's opinion, and carried out what he recommended. Finally, in his report of January 1800, the latter wrote: 'The masonry of Chirk Aqueduct is very perfect. I have seen no reason to recommend any deviation from the design . . .' Thus, with his approval, it was opened at the end of 1801.

* He seems to mean a damp-proof course.

Fig 15: Part of Pontcysyllte Aqueduct as it is today.

VI. Telford's *Life* on Chirk and Pontcysyllte

Telford seems not to have mentioned either aqueduct in his letters to Andrew Little, while the documents accompanying the *Oration* of 1805 have already been described. So we come to Telford's *Life*, where in one paragraph on pp 41–2 of the printed text a myth was created, that of Telford's Pontcysyllte.

He begins, however, with Chirk, where the printed account does not differ materially from the earlier versions:

> The Ceriog, or Chirk valley, is 710 feet in width; the banks are steep, with a flat alluvial meadow between them, through which the river passes. To preserve the canal level, the surface of its water must be maintained at 65 feet above the meadow, and 70 above the water in the river. There are 10 arches, each of which is 40 feet span. The first stone of this aqueduct was laid on the 17th June 1796. Previously to this time, such canal aqueducts had been uniformly made to retain the water necessary for navigation, by means of puddled earth retained by masonry; and in order to obtain sufficient breadth for this superstructure, the masonry of the piers, abutments and arches was of massive strength; and after all this expense, and every imaginable precaution, the frosts, by swelling the moist puddle, frequently created fissures, burst

97

Fig 16: Chirk Aqueduct, with the later railway viaduct behind.

Fig 17: Unusual view of Chirk Aqueduct taken from above. The second path on the near side has been taken out of use and the waterway fenced off for safety reasons.

98

the masonry, and suffered the water to escape, nay sometimes actually threw down the aqueducts; instances of this kind having occurred even in the works of the justly celebrated Brindley. It was evident that the increased pressure of the puddled earth was the chief cause of such failures; I therefore had recourse to the following scheme in order to avoid using it. The spandrills of the stone arches were constructed with longitudinal walls (as at Kirkcudbright Bridge), instead of being filled with earth, and across these the canal bottom was formed by cast-iron plates at each side, infixed in square stone masonry. Those bottom plates had flanches on their edges, and were secured by nuts and screws at every juncture. The sides of the canal were made water-proof by ashler masonry, backed with hard burnt bricks, laid in Parker's cement, on the outside of which was rubble stone work, like the rest of the aqueduct. The towing-path had a thin bed of clay under the gravel, and its outer edge was protected by an iron railing. The width of the water-way is 11 feet, of the masonry on each side, 5 feet 6 inches, and the depth of the water in the canal is 5 feet.

By this mode of construction, the quantity of masonry is much diminished, and the iron bottom plate forms a continued tie, and prevents the side walls from separation by lateral pressure of the contained water. There being a quarry of excellent flat bedded rubble-stone within a quarter of a mile of the site, and lime-kilns within two miles, the whole, with the exception of quoins, coping and lining the sides of the water-way, which are of ashler masonry, is of rubble work, laid in lime mortar; the materials and workmanship equally excellent. The edifice was completed in the year 1801, and is still in a perfect state; the total cost was £20,898.

This account leaves out the whole of the aqueduct's pre-history. We know that Jessop proposed an iron trough on 14 July 1795, after which Telford changed to rubble stone arches, for which he got Jessop's approval. The plan was then again changed to include an iron-plated bottom. So it was built, and in January 1800 Jessop saw it under construction and approved, saying that he saw no reason to recommend any deviation from the design. The text begins with the aqueduct in its form as built, and makes it seem that it had been so designed. We may notice, also, in the sentence beginning 'Previously to this time', the omission of the two iron trough aqueducts already in use, Outram's at the Holmes on the Derby Canal, and Reynolds' and Telford's at Longdon – the trough at Pontcysyllte had not then, of course, been begun.

So the *Life* moves to Pontcysyllte:

First version, entirely in Telford's hand

About 4 miles north of Chirk, the Aqueduct of Pontcysylte forms a still more important Object than that I have just described; the North Bank of the River Dee at this Place is very abrupt, but on the south the descent is more gradual, on account of gravelly earth being readily found from an adjacent Bank, it was found the most economical Plan to carry an Embankment of that material from the level of the waterway 500 yards to the depth of 75 feet, till there remained a distance of 1007 feet to pass over the River to the north Bank where the height is 127 feet; it therefore was a serious consideration [   ] to accomplish this passage at any reasonable expense; to Lock down on each side as originally intended I perceived

Second version, alterations seemingly in Rickman's hand italicised

About four miles north of Chirk, the Aqueduct of Pont y Cylte forms a more *striking* object than that *which* I have just described. The North bank of the River Dee at this Place is abrupt, in the South side the *acclivity* is more gradual; *and here* on account of gravelly Earth being readily procured from an adjacent Bank, it was found most economical Plan to *push out* an Embankment 1500 feet in length from the level of the Waterway *until its perpendicular height became* 75 feet; still a distance of 1007 feet of the canal *intervened before arriving* at the North bank, *and in the middle of this space the River Dee was 127 feet below the water level of the Canal, which was to be carried over it, and serious consideration was requisite in what manner* to

Printed version, further alterations presumably by Rickman alone

See Note A

About four miles north of Chirk, the Aqueduct of Pont-y-cysylte forms a still more striking object than that which I have just described. The north bank of the River Dee at this place is abrupt; on the south side the acclivity is more gradual; and here, on account of gravelly earth being readily procured from the adjacent bank, it was found most economical to push forward an earthen embankment, 1,500 feet in length from the level of the water-way of the canal, until its perpendicular height became 75 feet; still a distance of 1,007 feet intervened before arriving at the north bank, and in the middle of this space the River Dee was 127 feet below the water level of the canal, which was to be carried over it; therefore serious

First version, entirely in Telford's hand

was quite inadvisable, as it would have been losing Water on both sides the Valley, whereas there was not more than sufficient to supply the general Lockage from the Summit level. To construct an Aqueduct upon the Plan previously practised by Masonry Piers and turning Arches, at nearly 100 feet in height, of sufficient width and strength to afford a Puddled Water Way would have been an expensive and hazardous operation; necessity therefore obliged me to some safer and more economical mode of proceeding.

I had about that time carried the Shrewsbury Canal, by an Iron Trough, over the River Tern at about 16 feet above the level of the ground – finding this practicable, it occurred to me that there being

---

Second version, alterations seemingly in Rickman's hand italicised

accomplish this passage at any Reasonable expence. To Lock down on each side *50 or 60 feet by 7 or 8 Locks* as originally intended, I perceived was inadvisable, indeed impracticable, *as involving serious loss of* Water on both sides the Valley, whereas there was not more than sufficient to supply the *unavoidable* Lockage *and leakage* from the Summit level. To construct an Aqueduct upon the usual principles, by Masonry Piers and Arches 100 feet in height, of sufficient breadth and strength to afford room for a Puddled Water-way, would have been hazardous and *enormously* expensive: necessity therefore obliged me to contrive some safer and more economical mode of proceeding. I had about that time carried the Shrewsbury

---

Printed version, further alterations presumably by Rickman alone

consideration was requisite in what manner to accomplish this passage at any reasonable expense. To lock down on each side 50 or 60 feet by 7 or 8 locks, as originally intended, I perceived was indeed impracticable, as involving serious loss of water on both sides the valley, whereas there was not more than sufficient to supply the unavoidable lockage and leakage of the summit level. To construct an aqueduct upon the usual principles, by masonry piers and arches 100 feet in height, of sufficient breadth and strength to afford room for a puddled water-way, would have been hazardous, and enormously expensive: necessity obliged me therefore to contrive some safer and more economical mode of proceeding. I had about that

First version, entirely in Telford's hand

hard sandstone adjacent to Pontcysylte, that there could be no serious difficulty in building a sufficient number of square Piers to support a Cast Iron Trough of a proper [strength?] with Cast Iron Arched Ribs under it between the Piers. After close consideration, I had a Model made of two Piers, a Sett of Ribs, the Canal Trough, the Towing Path, side Railing, and all the flanches with all their nuts and Screw Pins and jointing complete.

The foundations of the River Piers are placed upon hard Sand Stone Rock, which form [a Coal Measure (deleted)] those on each bank are either on Coal measures or on firm Gravel; thus secure of good foundations, suitable Sandstone for the Masonry, the best of

Second version, alterations seemingly in Rickman's hand italicised

Canal by a cast Iron Trough over the River Tern at about 16 feet above the Level of the ground; finding this practicable, it occurred to me that there was hard sandstone adjacent to Pont y Cylte so that there could be no very serious difficulty in building a sufficient number of square Pillars *of sufficient dimensions to support* cast Iron Ribs [under?] between the Piers; after due consideration, I *caused* a Model to be made of two Piers, a Set *or compartment* of Ribs, the Canal Trough, the *Towing★* Path and side Railing, with the flanches, their Nuts and Screws, and jointing complete. The foundations of the River Piers, are placed upon hard sandstone Rock, those on each bank, are either on *alternating Coal Strata* or hard, firm Gravel; thus secure of good foundations, suitable Sand stone

Printed version, further alterations presumably by Rickman alone

See Note B

See Note C

time carried the Shrewsbury canal by a cast-iron trough at about 16 feet above the level of the ground; and finding this practicable, it occurred to me, as there was hard sandstone adjacent to Pont-y-cysylte, that no very serious difficulty could occur in building a sufficient number of square pillars, of sufficient dimensions to support a cast-iron trough, with ribs under it for the canal. After due consideration, I caused a model to be made of two piers, a set or compartment of ribs, the canal trough, the towing-path and side railing, with all the flanches, their nuts and screws and jointing complete. The foundations of the river piers are placed upon hard sandstone rock; those on each bank are either on alternating coal

★ Telford had here written 'Haling'; Rickman restores his original wording.

102

First version, entirely in Telford's hand

Iron a satisfactory model for the Iron Work★ and able experienced Workmen for the execution, I proceeded with confidence of ultimate success altho' the Undertaking was unprecedented, and generally considered hazardous.

The height of the Piers above the surface of low water in the River, is 121ft 6in, though size of entry at high water Line, is 20 feet by 12; at the top 13 by 7ft 6in; the upper 50 feet is hollow; the other walls being only 2 feet in thickness, with one Cross inner Wall. This mode not only throws the Centre of gravity lower in the Pier, and saves Masonry, but it insures perfect workmanship, because the back as well as the front of each Stone is instantly open to in-

Second version, alterations seemingly in Rickman's hand italicised

for the masonry, the best of Iron, a satisfactory model of the Iron Work, and able experienced Workmen. I proceeded with confidence of ultimate success, altho' the undertaking was unprecedented and generally considered hazardous.

The height of the Piers above the low water in the River, is 121ft, *their sections* at high Water is 20 feet by 12; and at the top 13 feet by 7ft 6in; To 70 feet elevation from the base they are solid; but the upper 50 feet is built hollow, the outer Walls being only two feet in thickness, with one cross inner Wall; this not only places the centre of gravity lower in the Pier, and saves Masonry, but insures good

Printed version, further alterations presumably by Rickman alone

strata or hard firm gravel. Thus secure of good foundations, suitable sandstone for the masonry, the best of iron, a satisfactory model of the iron work, and able experienced workmen, I proceeded with confidence of ultimate success, although the undertaking was unprecedented, and generally considered hazardous.

The height of the piers above the low water in the river is 121ft, their section at the level of high water in the river is 20 feet by 12 feet, at the top 13 feet by 7 feet 6 inches.† To 70 feet elevation from the base they are solid, but the upper 50 feet is built hollow; the outer walls being only 2 feet in thickness, with one cross inner wall; this not only places the centre of gravity lower in the pier, and saves

See
Note
D

★ Perhaps he had in mind the reduced-scale model now in the Waterways Museum, or perhaps a full-sized trial, as much as anything to get the construction sequence right and to train the erectors on the job.

† The actual dimensions are: at the base just above the plinth, 20ft 1in by 10ft; at the top, 13ft by 7ft 4in. These figures kindly supplied by the British Waterways Board.

First version, entirely in Telford's hand

spection; I have, ever since that time, had every tall Pier under my direction built hollow.

The width of the Water Way is 11ft 10in of which the haling path covers 4ft 8in, leaving 7ft 2in for the Boat, but the haling path stands upon Pillars under which the water flows freely, the Boat therefore passes easily.

The Stone Piers as will been [be seen] in Plate – are 18 in number, besides the two Abutments, they were all carried up to the level of 20 feet, and then the Scaffolding and gangways were raised to that level and the materials brought from the North Bank always beginning at the southern extremity and working back to the north bank.

Second version, alterations seemingly in Rickman's hand italicised

workmanship, as every side of each Stone is exposed; I have ever since that time, *caused* every tall Pier under my direction *to be thus* built. The width of the Water way is 11ft 10in of which the towing path covers 4ft 8in, leaving 7ft 2in for the boat, but the *towing* path stands upon Iron Pillars, under which the water fluctuates and recedes freely, the boat passes with ease; the Stone Piers are 18 in number, besides the two Abutment Piers; they are all built to the level of 20 feet, when the scaffolding and gangways were all at once raised to that level, and the material being brought from the north bank *the workmen always commenced* at the abutment pier, receding pier by pier to the north bank, *and by thus gradually ascending they felt*

Printed version, further alterations presumably by Rickman alone

masonry, but insures good workmanship, as every side of each stone is exposed. I have ever since that time caused every tall pier under my direction to be thus built.[*] The width of the water-way is 11 feet 10 inches, of which the towing-path covers 4 feet 8 inches, leaving 7 feet 2 inches for the boat; but as the towing-path stands upon iron pillars, under which the water fluctuates and recedes freely, the boat passes with ease. The stone piers are 18 in number, besides the two abutment piers; they were all built to the level of 20 feet, and then the scaffolding and gangways were all raised to that level, and the materials being brought from the north bank, the workmen always commenced at the most distant or south abut-

See Note E

[*] An asterisk in the printed text refers to a footnote; it is reprinted in full on pp 107–110.

First version, entirely in Telford's hand

The Workmen by this gradually ascending, had no more apprehension of danger when on the highest Scaffold, than when on the lowest; it luckily happened, however, that one man only fell during the whole of the operations, while building the Piers and putting up the Iron Work.

By referring to Plate – the general form and also the details of construction will be readily understood. It was opened in 1805, and has now been navigated 26 years with utility and safety; it has added a striking feature to the beautiful Vale of Llangollen, in which was formerly placed the fortress of the British Hero (Owen Glyndwr), but which cleared of its entangled Woods, is become the useful Line

---

Second version, alterations seemingly in Rickman's hand italicised

no more apprehension of danger when on the highest Scaffold, than when at first on the lowest, and one man only fell during the whole of the operations, in building the Piers and affixing the Iron Work upon their summit.

By referring to Plate – the general form and also the details of construction will be readily understood. *This singular aqueduct* was opened in 1805, and has now been navigated 26 years with facility and safety; *and thus has been* added a striking feature to the beautiful Vale of Llangollen, in which formerly *was the fastness of* Owen Glyndwr, but which now cleared of its entangled Woods, *contains* the useful line of intercourse between England and Ireland; *and the*

Printed version, further alterations presumably by Rickman alone

ment pier, receding pier by pier to the north bank; and by thus ascending from time to time in their work, they felt no more apprehension of danger when on the highest, than at first on the lowest gangways; one man only fell during the whole of the operations in building the piers, and affixing the iron work upon their summit, and this took place from carelessness on his part.

By referring to Plate 14, the general form, and also the details of construction, will be readily understood. This singular aqueduct was opened in 1805, and has now been navigated 28 years with facility and safety; and thus has been added a striking feature to the beautiful vale of Llangollen, in which formerly was the fastness of

First version, entirely in Telford's hand
of intercourse between England and Ireland; and the waters of the sacred Deva is rendered the means of distributing prosperity over the adjacent Lands of the Saxon. The whole Expence of the Aqueduct and the giant Embankment was only £47,069.6.7.

Second version, alterations seemingly in Rickman's hand italicised
Water drawn *from the once* sacred Deva *furnishes* the means of distributing prosperity over the adjacent Land of the Saxons.

The whole expense of the Aqueduct and the great Embankment was £47,069, *a moderate sum as compared with the attainment of its object which involved the fate of the Ellesmere Canal.*

Printed version, further alterations presumably by Rickman alone
Owen Glyndwr, but which, now cleared of its entangled woods, contains the useful line of intercourse between England and Ireland; and the water drawn from the once sacred Deva, furnishes the means of distributing prosperity over the adjacent land of the Saxons.

The whole expense★ of the aqueduct and great embankment was £47,018; a moderate sum as compared with what by any mode heretofore in practice, it would have cost.

Then follows, identical except for details of orthography etc, the following in all three texts; here I give that from the printed version:

The following inscription on a cast-iron plate, is inserted in the pier, next the south bank of the river.

See Note F

> The Nobility and Gentry of
> the adjacent Counties,
> having united their efforts with
> the great Commercial Interests of this Country,

★	£.	s.	d.
Expense of earthen embankment	8,570	15	8
Masonry	21,162	13	5½
Iron Work	17,284	17	5½

	£47,018	6	7

106

in creating an intercourse and union between
England and North Wales,
by a Navigable Communication of the Rivers
Severn, Dee and Mersey,
for the mutual benefit of Agriculture and Trade,
caused the first Stone of this Aqueduct of
PONT-Y-CYSYLTE
to be laid, on the 25th day of July 1795;
When RICHARD MYDDELTON, of Chirk, Esq. M.P.
one of the original Promoters of the
ELLESMERE CANAL,
was Lord of the Manor; and in
the Reign of Our Sovereign GEORGE THE THIRD;
When the equity of the Laws, and security of Property,
promoted the general welfare of the Nation;
While the Arts and Sciences flourished
under His Patronage, and
the conduct of civil life was improved
by His Example.

This inscription shows by whom, and in what spirit the general project originated, and never was a public work carried into effect with greater unanimity.

THOMAS TELFORD, F.R.S.L. & E. was Engineer.
MATTHEW DAVIDSON was Superintendent of the Work.
JOHN SIMPSON and JOHN WILSON executed the Masonry.
WILLIAM HAZLEDINE executed the Iron Work.
WILLIAM DAVIES made the Earthen Embankment.

I now quote in full the curious footnote (see p. 104)

See Note G

Mr. Telford had seen evidence of the weakness of masonry supports which in appearance promised the utmost durability. The fall of St. Chad's Church, described in a former note (p. 26), disclosed to him in a striking manner the structure of its pillars, which were of great diameter, but merely shells of masonry, filled with dry rubbish; nor indeed is such dangerous fallacy confined to ancient edifices, the rubble backing of the piers of Westminster Bridge (finished in the year 1745) scarcely supporting itself whenever the surface ashler work is removed for occasional repairs. Mr. Telford led the way in preventing much of this kind of fraud in bridge-building, by substituting longitudinal walls under the road-way, instead of filling the space with earth or rubbish; a great improvement, since adopted by all engineers. [*See* p. 27.] And whenever masonry piers are of sufficient dimensions to admit of apertures large enough for the convenience of the workman, and therefore also admitting subsequent examination of his workmanship, security is thus obtained, far more valuable than the questionable superiority of a solid mass, in which the true bearing and connexion of every stone is not of necessity brought to a test, as in a bonded wall.

Nothing in the history of masonry is more instructive than the duration of the Irish Round Towers, which will illustrate the excellent principle adopted by Mr. Telford; moreover they afford early instance of erecting such lofty buildings from within (avoiding the expenses of scaffolding), as has recently been practised with decided economy in constructing steam-engine chimneys.

An Irish round tower in some instances exceeds 100 feet in elevation, and they may be said to average at 90 feet. Their outward circumference is about 45 feet at the base, where the thickness of the wall is from 3 to 4 feet, lessening upwards in a due degree to the summit. The expense of such an edifice (if now built) would not exceed £.300 or £.400.

About 120 of these towers are known to have existed in Ireland, and 90 of them still remain in various stages of decay, with the exception of a few still perfect, to the very coping-stone of the roof. These slender edifices (some of them) have withstood the wind and the rain and casual injury during 1000 years; for although the too frequent exaggeration of Irish antiquaries and historians has created very general incredulity, and, in consequence, inattention to what is really true of the Western Island and of its comparative civilization at an early date, it is highly probable that these towers were built in the course of 500 years preceding the Norman conquest of England; that they were Christian edifices, and in reality the bell-towers of ancient churches, is proved by their constant connection with ruined churches and ancient burial-grounds in Ireland; and in Scotland, which received Christianity from Ireland, the church of Brechin affords example of a round tower annexed to the south transept, and now entered from it. Over the original entrance of this tower (closed with masonry when the church was built, and another doorway made) is sculptured, in rude relief, the Virgin Mother and her Babe.

The origin of these towers is from the Greek Church; and the Turkish disciples of Mahomet adopted them under the name of *Minarets*, as convenient for the same purpose of summoning the faithful to prayer, substituting merely the well-trained voice of the Mollah for a small bell, not permitted by their religion. In the decline of the Constantinopolitan empire, and long before the Turcoman invaders approached the capital, civilized occupations fled before them, and Greek architects were employed to adorn Italy with the magnificent churches and bell-towers of the middle ages. St. Mark's, at Venice, and its adjacent campanile, are perhaps some of the earliest productions of the Greek fugitives, who afterwards, in the confidence of their art, not only built round towers in Italy, but even built some of them purposely aslope from perpendicular, thus striking the mind of the beholder with an incongruous sensation of the known fact of their long duration and the appearance of immediate downfal.

There is no difficulty in supposing that some of the emigrant Greeks were attracted by the fame of Ireland, then the learned and the pious, to settle there, and imitate, in suitable manner, the parish churches of their native land in the East. Egypt, the most conspicuous member of the Greek church, was not likely to be deficient in religious edifices, and the most famous of her sainted hermits is distinguished as Simon Stilites, from his ascetic residence on the top of a pillar, in fact a round tower, connected with religious purposes. All things considered in a subject confessedly obscure, the best conjecture will perhaps attribute the date of the Irish round towers to the four or five centuries of which the reign of Charlemagne may be taken as the middle point.

The duration of these slender towers is worthy attention, not only of the antiquary, but much more of the architect. The first element of superior durability is seen in the large solid basement, or substruction, which was almost unavoidable from the position of the door-way at some distance from the ground; nor could the small diameter of the interior have admitted the entrance of timber spars for successive ladders, unless thrust upwards from a surface lower than the door-way. Among the 90 towers, which, in various states of decay, are still extant in Ireland, there are probably various specimens of the builder's art; the generality consist of that kind of careful masonry, called Spauled Rubble; in which small stones shaped by the hammer (in default of suitable stones at hand) are placed in every interstice of the larger stones, so that very little mortar is intermixed in the body of the wall, which is raised stage by stage of convenient height; the outside of spauled masonry especially presenting an almost uninterrupted surface of stone, supplementary splinters being carefully inserted in the joints of the undried wall.

The seemingly rude coverings of these towers are perhaps the best, that is, the most durable, ever devised by human wit. The arch familiar to the Greeks of the Lower Empire, could not be introduced where lateral abutment was impossible, and timber support was out of the question, so that the overlapping of flat stones consolidated by mortar into a hollow cone, was perhaps the only resource; and a few of these stone roofs still remain surmounted by their cap-stone. – A civil engineer, much connected with Mr. Telford's occasional missions to Ireland, has remarked, that the four windows (or narrow loop-holes) of these towers near the summit very exactly accord with the four points of the compass; but some of the towers have no more than two such windows; some more in number than four.

Here we have a text which suggests that Telford, judging a masonry aqueduct impracticable at Pontcysyllte, and having found one of iron practicable at Longdon, then set about designing the iron trough at the full length of 1007ft, building a model, choosing his iron and making sure experienced workmen would be available, presumably all in the period between 14 March 1795, when the Longdon aqueduct in iron was authorised by the Shrewsbury Canal committee, and 14 July 1795, when Jessop wrote his crucial report recommending the iron trough, or 10 August when the committee accepted the report and directed Telford to take action. The false impression having been given to the reader that, Longdon having been successful, Poncysyllte was immediately designed and planned, it naturally follows that the credit must be Telford's.

As my earlier chronology (p. 92) and analysis of responsibilities for Pontcysyllte aqueduct (p. 93) shows, the Telford/Rickman account makes little contact with reality. Let me note the major points. Each note is keyed to the relevant section.

NOTES

A. The argument of the first paragraph is curious. When Jessop wrote his original report in January 1792, he had foreseen a full-height aqueduct 970ft long and 126ft high (almost exactly Pontcysyllte's final dimensions of 1007ft × 126ft). He put the cost at £35,000. Should the level be dropped 24 ft, i.e. to 102ft, by using three locks at each end, the cost would fall to £21,286. These structures must have been intended in masonry, for iron troughs had not then been thought of, yet he made no suggestion that either was impracticable. He knew, as Telford must have done, that earlier engineers had built much higher masonry aqueducts e.g. the Pont du Gard, 155ft, or the 13th-century water-carrier to Spoleto in Italy, 700ft long and 270ft high. He was also a man careful with his estimates. I have suggested that Turner's original masonry aqueduct was at about 100ft, after which, perhaps early in 1795, it was dropped to 76ft. Probably however, the increased cost of locks would roughly have balanced the cheaper aqueduct. Yet Jessop's full-height figure of £35,000 compares with the actual cost of Pontcysyllte of £38,448 though the figures are only very roughly comparable. We note also Rickman's heightening of Telford's 'expensive' to 'enormously expensive'.

When Telford writes of 'an Aqueduct . . . at nearly 100 feet in height', he may be thinking of Jessop's original proposal, or of Turner's. He has forgotten the further drop to 76ft. Rickman did perceive this, and inserted 'lock down 50 or 60 feet', yet left the reference to '100 feet'.

Again, Telford was writing around 1831. Yet he can say that to build a 100ft masonry structure would have been 'expensive and hazardous', when Outram had done just that at Marple (100ft high, 309ft long), and opened it in 1800, before much had been done to Pontcysyllte. Others also built in his lifetime were Baird's at the Avon (86ft), Almond (76ft) and Slateford (75ft) (these with iron for the channel as at Chirk) on the Edinburgh & Glasgow Union, and Rennie's at Dundas and Avoncliff on the Kennet & Avon, and over the Lune at Lancaster. The argument seems designed to justify the choice of iron – which may have been correct, but not for the reasons Telford gives, for surely a masonry structure of 76ft would have been no great problem to Telford's masonry skills. After all, between 1820 and 1823 he himself built Cartland Crags road bridge near Lanark, 122ft high with three masonry arches of 62ft span, and Dean bridge at Edinburgh between 1829 and 1831. This had four 90ft span arches and a height above the Waters of Leith of 106ft.

B. Telford's paragraph on the Shrewsbury Canal cannot be true, for reasons already given earlier in this chapter. He was appointed engineer on 28 February 1795, and the iron aqueduct at Longdon was agreed on 14 March, Jessop's report recommending iron troughs at Pontcysyllte and Chirk was presented to the Ellesmere committee on 14 July. By that date Longdon was probably still in design stage with parts being tested, for it was not opened until March 1796. Therefore Telford could not have found it 'practicable' in any but a theoretical sense.

As for the model, it is almost unbelievable that it was designed and made before the crucial 14 July 1795 meeting, especially as its design differs so greatly from Longdon, itself still in formative stage. It must date from Pontcysyllte's design state. One cannot conceive Hazledine submitting a tender until he knew just how the ironwork would be cast and the sections erected. We know now,

111

thanks to photographs of the underside, that the ribbed design would allow the erection of the bare plates with only the flimsiest of scaffolding under, needed for access for bolting up the underside and the side-plates. Only then, after having had a major part in the discussions that decided the aqueduct's design, would Hazledine have submitted his tender and the detailed drawings upon which it had been based.

C. Here and onwards Telford is greatly telescoping time, so giving the impression that the planning of Pontcysyllte in detail was all done by him – presumably before authorization, certainly in a comparatively short time. But it was not; very little was done in planning until 1799, four years later than Telford is implying. To give one illustration; he talks of 'the best of iron, a satisfactory model of the iron work, and able experienced workmen'. But in 1795 almost certainly Hazledine's foundry at Plas Kynaston was not in existence (see p. 40) for in February 1797 John Wilkinson and William Reynolds were invited to tender for casting and erection; it was not until 17 March 1802 that Hazledine's tender was accepted.

D. The dimensions of the piers were not settled at once, and when they were, such evidence as we have (Jessop's letter of 26 July 1795 and his report of 24 January 1800) points to Jessop's having decided, but presumably after discussion with Telford, especially in view of his mason's experience. In the letter, he gives the original intended dimensions of the piers at the top as 10ft × 6ft. He proposes, mainly for safety reasons, '7 feet wide at the Top instead of 6 feet, and make them about 2 feet more in the other dimensions'. He seems to mean increasing the top dimensions from 10ft × 6ft to 12ft × 7ft. (See p. 41 for final dimensions.) In the report, he tells us that the bottom sections of those completed had been built solid; he now recommends that 'in what remains to be done they should be built hollow', each wall 2ft thick, the sides tied together with oak timbers for safety reasons.

Though stone later replaced timber for the inner cross walls, Telford does not take credit for the hollow-wall construction, he praises it, and says he will use it in future. Rickman in his final text follows Telford, but it is difficult to think of any reason for adding his long footnote other than to leave the impression, without clearly stating, that the credit was Telford's.

Rickman adds in the printed text a little bit of whitewash; Telford had recorded that one man had lost his life during construction; Rickman adds 'and this took place from carelessness on his part'. E. Telford here, quite rightly, specially mentions the design of Pontcysyllte, whereby the towpath is built over part of the waterway, so causing less resistance to boats than would be the case were they to be confined in a trough little wider than the boat.* It seems, however, not to have been Telford's idea. Whiles Clowes was still alive, he was building Berwick tunnel on the Shrewsbury Canal (intended for tub-boats 4ft 4ins wide) rather over 10ft wide, but without a towpath. At a committee meeting on 25 April 1794, the question was raised whether a towpath was needed. William Reynolds was asked to decide, and at the 4 July meeting he recommended a towpath. This, the first in Britain to be provided for a tunnel of any length (Berwick was 970yds), was 3ft wide, timber-built, overhung the canal, and rested on bearers set in the wall.

Though decided by Reynolds while Clowes was still engineer, the idea of transferring the improvement a year later to Longdon aqueduct occurred neither to Reynolds nor Telford. It was given a towpath alongside a narrow-width water channel. It probably had still not occurred to Jessop or Telford when the former wrote his letter to Telford on 26 July 1795, and said; 'I begin to think it may be better to have the Canal 9 feet wide & 5 feet deep, as was first intended ...' But in February 1797 the Shrewsbury Canal was opened for traffic. We can guess that the ease of passing boats through Berwick tunnel by means of the overhanging towpath gave Telford (he, probably not Jessop) the idea of adapting it for the not-yet designed ironwork of Pontcysyllte. The same feature was given to the two short tunnels on the Ellesmere Canal: Chirk and Ellesmere.

Rickman's adulation comes in again. Telford's 'It' becomes 'This singular aqueduct'; Telford's statement of the cost was first embellished with 'a moderate sum, as compared with the attainment of its object which involved the fate of the Ellesmere Canal'. This was then again altered to the printed version's: 'a moderate sum as compared with what by any mode heretofore in practice, it would have cost.'

---

* Mr I. Davidson has pointed out that hydraulic theory also explains the phenomenon, most important at Pontcysyllte, that the contrary flowing of water past a moving boat automatically forces the boat away from the aqueduct edge and towards the towpath. *Trans Newcomen Soc.* Vol 51, p.141.

F. Telford does not explain that the inscription placed on the foundation stone, laid in 1795, referred to the original lower-level masonry aqueduct, and so to the original course of the Ellesmere Canal.

The credits follow those issued with the 1805 *Oration* (see p. 48) except that the Royal Society letters are added after Telford's name, and John Wilson's has been added to that of John Simpson, maybe as an indirect tribute to a man who, until his death, had been contractor for Telford's last canal, the Birmingham & Liverpool Junction. I thought at first that Telford was implying that the list of personalities had been added to the plaque itself. It may have been. I can only say that its erection does not seem to be mentioned in the canal records, that I can find no other reference to it, and that it is not there now.* Did he hope that it would be erected after his death, and did protests made after publication of the *Life* prevent this?

G. The long footnote beginning with a reference to Telford's experience with the collapse of the tower of St. Chad's church, Shrewsbury and going on to a disquisition on Irish round towers, is entirely Rickman's. It strikes oddly, for Telford had in 1800 no recorded experience of Ireland, whereas Jessop[20] had had a very great deal ever since 1773. Rickman's assumption is that Telford had introduced the hollow wall system used for the upper part of Pontcysyllte's piers, but we have seen that it derives from Jessop's 1800 report.

Here our account ends. I hope my exploration has been to find and assess facts, not to denigrate or praise. If we turn back to the tabulation of pages 92–3, do not answers become clear to questions often asked? Pontcysyllte can fairly be described as Jessop's as are the Kennet & Avon's aqueducts as Rennie's, but it cannot be called Telford's. I myself prefer to write, as for so long I have, 'Jessop's and Telford's'. One must therefore regard the *Life*'s account of the Ellesmere Canal as an example of what can result when an elderly and justly famous man finds himself enclosed within walls built long before when he found temptation too hard to resist. There are few of us who in youth can correctly assess the results of actions which turn out later to have affected our whole lives.

---

* Mr C. Brown, BWB Section Inspector, kindly had the pier carrying the plaque specially searched in August 1986.

Chapter 6

The Caledonian Canal: Lines of the Truth

I begin with a short account of the origin of the Caledonian Canal and its building, up to the time of Jessop's withdrawal from the works in 1812 on account of age and infirmity, and his death soon afterwards.

In 1801 Telford[1] was asked by the government to report upon what public works in the Highlands might help to discourage emigration. He was probably chosen because, as surveyor and engineer to the British Fisheries Society, he had reported on the North West as long ago as 1790. One subject he was told to examine was the often suggested canal[2] through the Great Glen from the east to the west coast that, at 10ft depth, had been surveyed by James Watt in 1773. His first[3] report, written in October 1801, said:

> I am convinced that a navigation may be formed from Inverness to Fort William of the description that is wanted. The line is very direct, and I have observed no serious obstacle in any part of it. The whole rise between the shores is trifling, and on the summit there is an inexhaustible supply of water. The Entrances from the Navigation into the Sea, are immediately in deep water, good anchoring ground, and in places of perfect safety at Inverness and Fort William.

He was here working on a canal of 50ft bottom, 100ft top width, and 20ft depth. His locks would have an 8ft rise, and these he thought might be turf-sided and cost £5,000 each, there being plenty of water.

Sent back to the Highlands in 1802, he reported fully on 15 March 1803[4] on five subjects, the canal among them. In a question he put to the Highland Society of Scotland he says: 'I have for the sake of distinction, named this Navigation "the Caledonian Canal"'. Finally, he writes: 'My Estimate of the Expence of forming this

Navigation is nearly £350,000, and the time required to complete it would probably be about seven years.

The government committee concerned then examined a number of expert witnesses, among them Rennie and Jessop.[5] Rennie said firmly that the locks should be lined with stone, and estimated them at £14,000 each, and the whole canal – perspicaciously – at £600,000–£700,000 'at least'. Jessop put his locks, also of masonry, at £10,000 each on average, but in a letter to Telford subjoined to the report said that the figure was calculated to be on the safe side.

Using this figure, when Jessop was asked whether he could estimate the canal's likely cost if it were for craft drawing 18ft, he replied:

> Under the favourable circumstances of ground tolerably even, and the soil moderately good, I should suppose it might cost about £22,000 a mile, including the Locks, Bridges and Canal, and other necessary works, but making no allowance for any extra works. I am also supposing that you have the opportunity of chusing your ground, so that with about 15 feet cutting, you may make Banks that will retain 20 feet water.

This estimate did not of course include land purchase costs. The committee reported that they were 'convinced of the practicability, as the importance, of the work'. Their report convinced Parliament, and a preliminary Bill[6] for this great state canal went rapidly through both Houses without opposition in July 1803.

The Act had named commissioners,★ of the nature of an executive committee, who moved quickly. Early in August they met Telford to draw up his instructions. He was to go to Scotland

> to make the necessary Surveys, and set out the Line of a Canal ... examining the navigation of the several Lochs or Lakes, and making proper trials of the intermediate ground through which the Canal was intended to pass; and also to expedite the Plans and Notices required by the Standing Orders of the House of Commons, in order to the making application for a regular Canal Act in the present Session ...

He was also to begin the excavation of the two entrance basins, open quarries, order materials and machinery, and draw up plans for financial control, accounting and correspondence.

★ One of whom was Sir William Pulteney, included as concerned with the British Fisheries Society.

Telford then left for Scotland, where he stayed till the middle of October. However the committee,

Thinking it our duty, in the prospect of so important an Undertaking, to omit no means of enabling ourselves to form an accurate judgment as to the practicability of the proposed Work, and the probable expence of executing it, We took measures as early as the 4th of August, for obtaining the opinion and assistance of Mr. William Jessop, another eminent and experienced Engineer . . . [7]

I do not know why Jessop was chosen. The commissioners may have liked the way he had given his earlier evidence, and the fact that his estimate and Telford's were in line, whereas Rennie's might have suggested extravagance. Or possibly because of his surveys of the only navigation in the British Isles that already combined lakes, canal sections and a river – the Shannon.

It had been intended that Jessop should be present at the briefing sessions in early August, but the commissioners' letter of 4 August 1803 found him away from home. When he replied, he did not seem to know the major part he was destined to play, for he said:

When my humble Services may in any way be useful to the Commissioners, I shall be happy in receiving their Commands and in obeying them, so far as I can consistent with prior Engagements. [8]

The Commissioners then tried again, but Jessop was away from home. Meanwhile, on 27 September, Telford, already in Scotland, wrote to John Rickman, secretary to the Commissioners:

As the idea of Mr. Jessop being consulted was suggested before I left London I was in hopes, if his coming down had been considered necessary, that he would have been here by this time, in which case he would have accompanied me along the whole Line from this place to Fort William, for which place I sett out tomorrow morning.

It is now late in the season for him to examine the Line, and I am obliged to be in Shropshire by the middle of October. But it is possible that Mr. Jessop may not judge it absolutely necessary to view the Line. I can shew him a correct Map of the Line of the Canal, with a section of the Ground; I can describe the nature of the Soil in each District with the situation and quality of the material for Building. He can examine Mr. Simpson an Eminent and reputable Builder, who has examined these matters very carefully, and with whom Mr. Jessop has been acquainted for many years, he can also examine Mr. Howell who took the levels and made the surveys for me, and Mr. Jessop is likewise acquainted with him. If after all this, Mr. Jessop should think it necessary to view the ground, the doing this early in spring would be more advisable after we have opened some quarries and proved the ground near the entrance to the sea. But if the Commission and Mr. Jessop determine upon his coming North immediately, he will be shown the ground by Mr. Wilson, who will be either at Fort William or Inverness.[9]

Whereupon the Commission wrote again to ask Jessop to meet them, and again he could not:

I have been peculiarly unlucky in being two or three times disappointed of the honor of attending at the meeting of the Commissioners; and it coming now to my turn to serve the office of Mayor of this Borough for the ensuing Year, and the 4th of October happening to be the Day fixed for holding the Sessions for the Borough I cannot be in Town till after that Day.[10]

However, he was free 'after next week', so Rickman was told to write to tell Jessop to go to Scotland to examine the line himself, 'and that whether he meet with Mr. Thomas Telford or not he proceed immediately to survey the proposed Line of the Canal and also the proposed Basins at each end of it'.[11] He met Telford in mid-October, and proceeded on his survey. On 25 November the Commissioners had a letter from Jessop, as a result of which they told Telford to send him at Newark

the Section of the Line of the Canal and such accts as he may have received of trials which may have been made by Boring in several part of the Line, since he left Scotland.[12]

This Telford did, and on 14 December the two engineers met the Commissioners to report orally. After they had 'stated generally that upon the result of the trials and observations which they had made . . . no material objection or difficulty occurred to prevent its execution', they were asked to make a final report before February 1804.

On 25 January 1804 Telford had written to Rickman that 'To-morrow I set off on purpose to have an interview with Mr. Jessop, and prepare the report to the Board'.[13] However, the report was dated from Newark on 30 January and was signed by Jessop alone, a little after his fifty-ninth birthday. It was central to the enterprise, for his was the estimate upon which it went ahead. His figure was £474,531 excluding the cost of land, for a canal of 50ft bottom width and 90ft at top (this last figure being later changed to 110ft). Locks, now thought to be 23, would average £7,449 'exclusive of digging the Foundation and backing it with Earth'; this cost was later taken at £288, making £7,737 per lock. He had in mind masonry locks, each to be built separately, for he is maintaining his dislike of staircases, though later he had to give way for economy reasons. The locks were to be 152ft × 38ft, and the canal 20ft deep.

Jessop sent his report to Telford, who on 2 February wrote a covering letter. Both then went to Rickman for the Commissioners' meeting on the 6th. In his letter Telford, explaining that trial borings had been made and pits sunk along the line and at each end, went on:

> The particulars of these experiments have been regularly communicated to Mr. Jessop, as well as every information which appeared to be useful; and I have likewise had frequent Interviews with him in order to explain matters more fully:– Under the circumstances he has made out the Report and Estimate which I have here inclosed.

On the west the canal would start with a sea-lock at Corpach, then rise by a flight of eight at Banavie and run by several aqueducts to Loch Lochy, which was to be entered by the old bed of the Lochy, this river being given a new channel. The level of the loch was to be raised 12ft, to reduce the height of the deep cutting that was still necessary at Laggan to bring the canal in level with the bed of Loch Oich, which would itself need deepening. A weir was to be built and a new channel cut to allow the loch water to discharge into the River Spean instead of the Lochy.

From Loch Oich the line would follow, and in part use, the bed of the River Oich to Fort Augustus, where there would be problems in building locks because of the porous soil of gravel and sand, and in constructing the lowest of them 24ft below summer level in Loch Ness. It would need, said Jessop, 'the cutting a new Channel for the River through Rocky Ground at Fort Augustus, and making a Coffer Dam there for inclosing the Lock Pit'. At the loch's eastern end the River Ness would have to be dredged at its entrance to Loch Dochfour, which would itself have to be kept at the same level as Loch Ness. Thence a canal would be built to Muirtown, where four locks would take it to a huge basin to be built to serve Inverness. Thence the line would continue to the eastern entrance (at first to be at Kessock, then switched to Clachnaharry), where a coffer dam would be needed to build the sea-lock. The canal was to be cut from

119

each end, so that completed sections and locks could be used for transport when building the line further inland.

For their work so far Telford, whose charges were always 3 guineas a day, was now paid £667 18s 2d, and 'William Jessop, for his Survey, Report and Estimate, and for his Travelling Expenses', £209 15s, his rate being 5 guineas a day.

On 9 February the Commissioners met again, and minuted:

> The report and Estimate signed by Mr. Jessop, being considered as a sufficient foundation for the intended application to Parliament for further Grant and Powers, the Board proceeded to consider a draft of the petition . . . the draft of the proposed Bill, and the alterations therein proposed by Messrs. Jessop and Telford having been examined by the Board, it is referred to Mr. Mundell to insert the necessary corrections . . .

Jessop and Telford were then asked to prepare a joint statement of the financial grants that would be needed from year to year 'to complete the Canal as expeditiously as possible'.[15] On the 18th they provided an estimate of the current year's probable expenditure.

On 14 June 1804, Jessop appeared before the Lords committee on the second and principal Caledonian Bill:

> Mr. William Jessop, Engineer, proves the Estimate of the Expence of the Undertaking, and that it amounts to £474,531. Mr Thomas Telford, Surveyor, proves the Estimate of the Expence of the Land necessary to be purchased, and that it amounts to £15,000. Mr. Telford proves the other allegations of the Preamble . . .

The engineering estimate is signed by Jessop alone, that for land by Telford alone.

A little earlier, just before a Commissioners' meeting on 7 June, Telford had written to Rickman:

> . . . in a business of the magnitude of the Caledonian Canal, in order, as much as possible to ensure success, and avoid blame, it is prudent and adviseable to have every matter considered with great care before it is entered upon. And the Nature of the Soil, and the quality of the materials having now been sufficiently proved for the purpose of determining the precise situation, forms dimensions and values of each sort of work; It would be a great satisfaction to my mind, as well as an additional evidence to the Board, to have the assistance and advice of Mr Jessop, while in Scotland determining the above measures.[16]

On 7 June 1804, therefore, the Commissioners resolved

that Mr. Jessop should again visit the Line of the intended Navigation in concert with our Engineer, Mr Telford, in order that they might jointly inspect the progress of the works already commenced, and reexamine all the particulars of their former Survey; that they might determine the proper situation of each Lock on the whole Line of the Canal, and as far as possible fix the situation, dimensions and construction of the Bridges, Culverts, and other necessary works; and also that they might take into particular consideration the manner in which it would be most convenient to connect the Line of the Canal with the several Lochs or Lakes forming part of the intended navigation, and also settle the price of labour, and the mode in which the several works would be most advantageously lett in Lots to the Workmen, or otherwise executed in the best and safest manner.

The following day Telford proposed the appointment of resident staff and addressed a formal letter to Jessop putting forward names and duties of men 'as have to my own and your knowledge, for ten years past, been employed upon Works of a similar nature'; in fact mostly men from the Ellesmere Canal works. Matthew Davidson was to superintend the Clachnaharry end, John Telford (no known relation) the Corpach end. Jessop is then asked whether the salaries previously mentioned of 150 guineas each, plus a house and travelling expenses, were adequate for the superintendents, Jessop's reply[17] agrees to the appointments, and suggests £200 per year each for the superintendents. As for John Simpson, proposed in charge of construction, 'I know Mr. Simpson well'.

On 11 June a paper, 'Propositions to the Board by Messrs Jessop and Telford',[18] was sent in, setting out seven points that would need attention, to all of which the Commissioners agreed. Meanwhile, the two engineers were to consider the difference in cost of building varying sizes of lock to accommodate different-sized frigates and merchant ships. On the 14th, their statement was considered.

In his estimate annexed to their first report, Jessop had taken the lock size as 152ft × 38ft,

these dimensions having been deemed amply sufficient for the reception and passage of West-India and Baltic ships, and for Frigates not exceeding Twenty-eight Guns in force.

They now reported that at very small additional cost, the popular-sized 32-gun frigates and the largest ships trading to the Baltic could be accommodated. The Board therefore decided that the locks should be increased to 170ft × 40ft, canal dimensions remaining as before: 110ft wide at top, 50ft at bottom, and 20ft deep. Jessop's estimated lock cost of some £7,737 was now increased to £8,088.

At their meeting on 18th, the Board set out their 'Instructions to be observed by Messrs. Jessop and Telford respecting their proceedings in determination upon the different works . . .' These were an enlarged version of the 'Propositions' they had themselves submitted, and included everything concerned with setting out the line of canal, settling lock sites, wharves, turning places, bridges, culverts, weirs, the number and size of steam engines required, the method of letting contracts and their prices, and rules for the superintendents' conduct. Policy matters were therefore for practical reasons to be for joint decision and report. Separate instructions were set out for Telford alone in Appendix E of their second report, authorising the appointment of agreed staff, details of contract methods, and providing for monthly reports.[19]

Thus far, for the whole Scottish enterprise of roads, bridges, harbours and canal, Telford had been sole engineer. But now the Caledonian Canal had become a separate entity. Telford seems to have hoped that he would be given chief responsibility for it, but in the few days following 25 January 1804, Jessop had outmanoeuvred him. He was older, at that time Telford's senior on the Ellesmere Canal and, much more, at the height of his reputation as Britain's premier civil engineer.[20] I suspect that Telford's wording in his letter of that date suggests that he hoped to get Jessop's agreement to his draft report, and then to sign it himself. Instead, Jessop firmly took over. He wrote the final report and signed it, making it clear that he alone as senior engineer was taking full responsibility. Then follows Telford's letter to Rickman of 2 February, perhaps a last-ditch effort to explain how much Jessop's report owed to him; but by 9 February he had already lost, for the Commissioners had minuted that it was Jessop's report and estimate that had decided them to apply to Parliament for an Act.

In his letter to Rickman before the Commissioners' meeting on 7 June 1804, Telford had not given up, for he asks for Jessop's 'assistance and advice', and they then referred to Telford as 'our Engineer', presumably because he attended their meeting. But on 14 June Jessop appeared before the Lords committee on the Bill. He now took sole responsibility, and he alone was called 'Engineer', Telford being 'Surveyor'. This last may have been correct in terms of his evidence on the Bill but, as we shall see, Telford was to act, deservedly, as Jessop's engineering second-in-command. On 29 June the second Caledonian Canal Act received the royal assent. Telford had, however, sole charge of the huge scheme of road and bridge building he was to carry out over the following years.

Jessop, rising 60, went to Scotland in August 1804 with Telford. Whilst there, he wrote, 'Instructions from Mr Wm Jessop Civil Engineer to Mr John Telford, for marking out the Caledonian Canal'[21]. He also provided a number of drawings. Three sectional drawings of the proposed canal have been copied, including his signature and the date of August 1804; three are similar but unsigned.[22] Accompanying them are detailed instructions for marking out the line. The most important is *Plan and Elevation of the Sea Lock on the Caledonian Canal*, signed 'W. Jessop Aug. 1804', seemingly in his own hand. A small portion of the large sea-lock drawing has been copied by John Telford into his Notebook. Others survive from this period which can be attributed to Jessop. One is an unsigned lock drawing, *Section of a Forebay of a Lock on the Caledonian Canal*, in his unmistakable style. Another, dated 1804, *Sketch of the Ground Occupied by the Caledonian Canal through the Lands of Muirtown*, is a probability. A third, *Culvert for the River Loy*, is signed and dated August 1804.[23] More may yet be found.

Great tidal water ship locks at Corpach and Clachnaharry would in August 1804 have offered Jessop challenges, but no fears. His Ringsend docks in Dublin had been opened back in 1796; the Import dock of the West India system on London's Thames completed in 1802, with the Export dock well advanced; and Bristol docks begun. Telford at that date could show nothing comparable.[24]

On 6 November Telford wrote to Rickman: 'I have made out a draft of Report Jessop and self and shall transmit it to him for examination and signature after which it shall with some papers annexed be sent to you.'[25] This report of 29 November went in considerable detail into the state of construction, the financial arrangements they had made, and wage and price levels. As agreed the previous year, Telford was also to visit the works every spring and autumn for a thorough financial check. The report goes on to say Telford was placing contracts for timber and ironwork, including railways, with 'Iron-masters in Denbighshire, Derbyshire and Aberdeenshire',[26] and buying materials-carrying sloops and

123

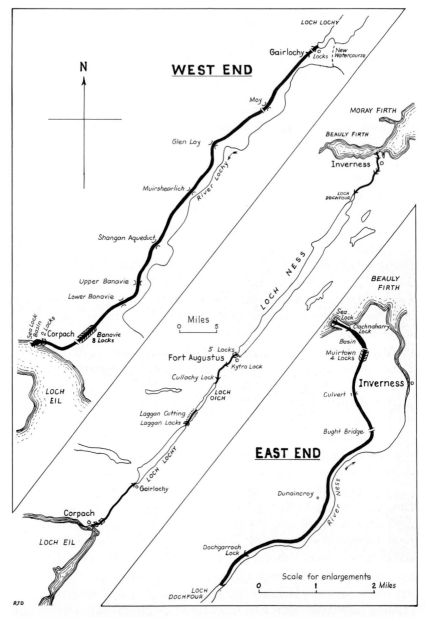

Fig 18: The Caledonian Canal.

steam engines. Their report included a decision to build most locks 'in clusters, so as to make a considerable saving in the expence of erection' (i.e. to build staircases), and a consequential decision to lengthen such locks to 180ft.

On their autumn 1804 inspection Jessop and Telford had had to postpone consideration of some points. Telford had also written to Rickman from Corpach on 26 April 1805:

> I shall be able to state pretty fully on the head of Prices, but I could do it more profitably after my return to England, and it would be more satisfactory to me, to have shewn my statements to, and taken Mr. Jessop's experience and assistance upon a point where he is materially concerned . . . I have made an arrangement with Mr. Jessop to examine the whole of the works in August or September next.[27]

The Board agreed.

On 15 September, Telford wrote to Rickman from Clachnaharry

Fig 19: Western Entrance. The Banavie 8-lock flight of locks comes in at the foot. There follow road and rail bridges, after which the canal curves to the right to fall by two locks to Corpach basin and the final sea-lock. Lock Eil is to the right, the sea to the left. The masonry of these three locks was also reported complete in 1812.

that 'Mr. Jessop is . . . arrived, and I have with him examined the works at this place, they are going on well'.[28] They now altered the line at the eastern end, deciding to divert the River Ness by an embankment into a newly-dug channel in order to use part of its old bed for the canal, and so get rid of the difficulty of the Ness's current in flood-time.

A drawing exists, *Section of the Cut from the New River thro' the Rock at Fort Augustus*, 1805, which includes a measurement of the surface level of Loch Ness on 23 September 1805. It seems to be Jessop's, and the date is of the time when he and Telford were on the Canal.

On 27 September Telford wrote again to Rickman:

> Mr. Jessop and I have been at Corpach, and we have carefully examined the Western portion of the Canal . . . we are now engaged in making arrangements respecting the Works between Loch Beauly and Loch Ness.[30]

They reported in November 1805. A barge had been built to carry 'the Dredging Machine and Steam Engine' to deepen Lochs Oich and Dochfour, the machine itself having been designed by Jessop and built, along with the steam engine, at Butterley and shipped at Hull for Inverness. It was intended to start work in the spring of 1806. Butterley also provided considerable lengths of contractors' railways and waggon wheels: £4,687 had been spent on them by 1807.

As regards bridges,

> On the Caledonian Canal it is intended to construct Bridges similar to those at the West-India Docks, and which have been imitated in Cast-Iron at the London Docks; they swing horizontally to each side of the Canal or Lock.

Jessop being engineer of the West India Docks at the time must have suggested the design[31] which originated with Ralph Walker, his resident engineer there.

After his spring 1806 visit, Telford reported that the first lock to be completed (except for its gates), that next above the sea-lock at Clachnaharry, had been built within Jessop's estimate.[32] For his work from the inception of the canal to the end of 1805, the canal's birth years, Jessop was paid £635 5s in all, including travelling expenses.

Jessop and Telford met again at Inverness on 19 September 1806, and their report[33] details the progress made. The Commissioners' spring report added that the two Corpach locks above the sea-lock had been built for under Jessop's price, but that single locks in future were likely to run at about £500 above, presumably because of the rise in the masonry price. It is perhaps worth noting, as we watch the various aqueducts being built along the line, that at no time were any in iron suggested: they are always of stone.

Next autumn the two engineers met again to review progress, as they did again a little later in the year 1808.[34] On this occasion they began their survey at Corpach on 1 November, and completed it in a fortnight. They now changed their minds on an important matter. They had intended to build both sea-locks by carrying rubble from excavations inland to form two projecting piers. Within the space between they intended to erect cofferdams, and then build the sea-locks inside them. This method succeeded (though only after great damage by storms) at Corpach, but not at Clachnaharry. They reported:

> On the shore at Clachnaharry, both the Mounds have been advanced so far as to embrace a portion of the space which was to have occupied by a Coffer-dam; but as the weight of the earth employed has caused these Mounds to sink considerably into the mud, it has suggested to us the idea of covering the whole space between them with earth and the rubbish form the neighbouring Quarry, so as to form it into an artificial Peninsula, for the purpose of so compressing or squeezing out the mud as to make it a firm foundation for a Lock, and thus save a considerable portion of the expense of a Coffer-dam.

In their covering report the Commissioners paid Telford a tribute:

> The steady progress . . . has evinced the prudence and foresight of the arrangements which were at first established by our Engineer Mr Telford, and the punctual observance of his Regulations by the Superintendants employed under him . . .

On 27 May 1809 the Commissioners,

> taking notice of the considerable degree of forwardness of the several works on the Canal near Clachnaharry and Corpach, and that the Expenditure now approaches to a Moiety of William Jessop's estimate of 1803–04,

direct him and Telford to compare what has been done with the estimate, allowing for the larger locks and the Clachnaharry sea mound and other alterations, and to do a new estimate of the cost of completing the canal.[35]

Jessop and Telford met again on 8 October 1809, and spent ten days together on the line.[36] Their change of plan at Clachnaharry was going well:

> As we have discovered by boring, that the Side-banks [of the Mound ...] have settled about eleven feet into the mud, we have directed that upon the middle space where the Lock itself will be placed ... the Earth shall be raised some height above the Level of the Side-banks, in order, by this additional weight, the more speedily and effectually to consolidate the Mud.

This very early example of pre-consolidation, coupled with pre-loading, proved to be brilliantly successful, and the lock was finished in 1812. This sea-lock, and the great embankment 1427ft (435 metres)* long at median line that links it to the land, is an extraordinary engineering work that has been too little regarded. Telford described it in a letter of 14 July 1812 to Baron von Platen in Sweden:

> Mr Davidson ... has just completed the Tide Lock here [at Clachnaharry], which is advanced above 400 Yards into the Sea and placed upon a soft Mud above 60 feet deep...[37]

With £250,000 spent by 1809 the two engineers now estimated[38] a further £300,000 would be needed to complete the canal plus the cost of land for the middle district – in spite of the need to increase some wages, still not much above Jessop's original figure of just under £500,000. The Commissioners were pleased, and wrote:

> we think that praise is justly due to Messrs Jessop and Telford for the accuracy of their Calculations, and likewise to the Superintendents and other Persons employed by Mr Telford, for their judicious arrangements, and faithful execution of their various duties.

For the years 1803–09 inclusive, Telford had been paid £1,858 10s and Jessop £1,329 15s.

Seemingly from about this time, the engineers were choosing to make increasing use of iron instead of good timber, so scarce in the Highlands and expensive to import, both for bridges and locks. While he was in Scotland in 1810, for instance, Jessop designed

---

* The length is taken from the railway bridge to the embankment's rounded end beyond the outer gates of the sea-lock. I use it by courtesy of Mr David Telford of the British Waterways Board.

Fig 20: Clachnaharry embankment and sea-lock, little-known wonder of the waterways. The sea-lock itself with its accompanying lock-house is at the foot of the picture. Then the entirely artificial great basin leads to a swing railway bridge, the first canal lock and Clachnaharry yard.

Fig 21: View in the opposite direction. Coming down to the left are Muirtown locks. The line swings left past Muirtown basin to Clachnaharry yard, the last canal lock and the railway bridge. There Clachnaharry

130

swing-bridges for the canal[39] with an iron framework filled in by timbers. A year later Butterley ironworks were supplying lock iron-work, for on 10 December 1811 Alexander Easton wrote to Telford: 'I have had notice from Mr. Jessop that part of the Iron work for the gates was sent to Liverpool'.[40]

Jessop's and Telford's report of October 1810[41] records straightforward progress. Copies also survive of two instructions, each of this date, one to Matthew Davidson, the other to Alexander Easton and his subordinates.[42] They are lists of things the engineers were to attend to over the following year, and each is signed first by Jessop and then by Telford. They show, perhaps, that although the detail is probably Telford's, Jessop is taking a major share of responsibility as first signatory, and that Telford is willing that he should do so.

A year later, in 1811,[43] Clachnaharry Lock is standing firm, and 'justifies the mode which was adopted to consolidate the soft Mud upon that Shore'. The engineers were now beginning to plan the works of the middle district:

> We have carefully examined the ground near Fort-Augustus, and have given directions for workmen to be employed in making Trial-pits and bore holes, to enable us to determine the precise site of the Locks . . .

In 1812 an employee accused Easton, who had succeeded John Telford as superintendent at Corpach, of fraud and collusion with master workmen in measuring work. Rickman wanted Jessop to take part in an enquiry, and wrote to James Hope, law agent at Edinburgh,

> He [Telford] is not without hope that Mr Jessop may be prevailed upon to travel northwards, and today I wrote to him . . . to urge the matter . . . as much as possible . . . this matter resting rather on the *Reputation* of the Judges, and especially *Highland Reputation*, than on any qualities however excellent if not recognised by all.[44]

From which we may take it that Jessop had such a reputation with the men working on the canal. On 17 October Hope wrote to Rickman: 'Mr. Telford has heard from W. Jessop who is to set off to Corpach and meet him there on the 25th October'.[45]

A formal enquiry with two magistrates took place on 27 October. The report, signed by the magistrates and Jessop, completely exonerated Easton. The story is revealing: that the workmen on the canal so trusted this Englishman, Devonian by birth, Midlander by adoption, that the elderly Jessop, so near death, extended his time at Corpach on his last visit because he felt it to be his duty as senior engineer; and that Telford, who so prided himself upon his good relations with subordinates, wanted him to come. Hughes' remark in his *Memoir* is borne out: 'many veterans of the profession still living, who, having been engaged on Jessop's great works . . . have not ceased to regard him with a kind of religious awe . . .'[46]

Jessop and Telford also signed a joint report[47] on the canal, but given the precarious state of the older man's health, it is likely to be largely Telford's work. It tells us that the masonry of the sea-lock at Clachnaharry had been completed, and its timber gates were being made. The next lock to it, the four to Muirtown (Inverness) and most of the canal to Loch Ness were finished. Then nothing at Fort Augustus and little in the middle district. A good deal from Loch Lochy had been done, including much of the deep cutting, and most of the aqueduct work. Banavie locks were finished except for gates, and so was the line thence to Corpach and the sea. Of Banavie the report said: 'The Masonry of the Great Chain of Locks is in a perfect state', and of Corpach: 'The Masonry of the Corpach Locks

Fig 22: The Caledonian Canal Report for 1812, signed by Jessop and Telford, reported: 'The Masonry of the Great Chain of Locks is in a perfect state'.

and Tide Lock is also perfect; and the Gates of the latter have been made and hung, and are excellent of their kind'.

The *Eleventh Report*, dated October 1813, was signed by Telford alone, but responsibility for an important policy change is attributed to both engineers, presumably because Jessop was still alive, though incapacitated[48].

> The Masonry of the Abutments of the Muirtown Bridge is finished . . . it was originally intended to make the permanent Bridge of Wood; but the present expense of forming it of Oak Timber in that remote district, and the consideration of future Repairs, induced Mr. Jessop and myself to have recourse to Iron . . .
>
> Proper Oak Timber has been procured for the Lower and Upper Gates of the Muirtown Chain of Locks: but the repeated disappointments and delays experienced in attempting to procure Oak Timber of the requisite shape, dimensions, and quality, have led Mr. Jessop and myself to adopt Cast-Iron, which will not only obviate the difficulties now felt on the Caledonian Canal, but being a British Material and Manufacture, inexhaustible in quantity, and by means of Canals, accessible in every quarter, it will we are convinced in future prove as serviceable in large Lock and Dock-Gates here and elsewhere, as I have already in many years experience found it to be in Gates of smaller dimensions, as well as in large Bridges and Aqueducts.[49]

In the year's cumulative accounts, we may notice:

> Thomas Telford, for general Superintendence and Management, 1803–1813 – £2,464 7s.
>
> William Jessop, for Attendance on the Business of the Caledonian Canal, 1803–1812 – £2,057 3s.

Samuel Hughes[50] made two statements of his opinion of Jessop's contribution to the Caledonian Canal:

> It is singular that in the notice of Mr. Jessop in the first volume of the Engineers' Transactions, no mention is made of the Caledonian Canal, although it is perfectly notorious that he was the senior engineer of that work, that the plan and main features of its execution were settled by him even before consulting with Mr. Telford, and that during the progress of the works he continued to be the chief engineer, in which capacity he made an annual report to the Commissioners.

and

> My own opinion, derived from the information of several gentlemen

whom I have consulted, as being the most impartial of those possessing any knowledge of this subject, is this, that although Mr Jessop did originally design the works, and settle the principal points, yet in the execution of these works, which were afterwards much varied from the original intentions, these two engineers are entitled to share alike in all the merits and defects which belong to them. It will add to the weight of this opinion to state, that it coincides with that of Mr. George May, of Inverness, the present talented engineer of the Caledonian Canal Commissioners.

This conforms to a near contemporary statement, that published in 1817 in Vol XI of the *Edinburgh Encyclopaedia*, which contained a biography of Jessop:

> For several years, previous to his death, he acted jointly with Mr. Telford in conducting the great Caledonian Canal in the north of Scotland, and that engineer embraced every opportunity of acknowledging, in the warmest manner, the advantages and satisfaction he derived from the able, upright, and liberal conduct of his enlightened colleague and friend,

a remark we have seen to be true from Telford's official correspondence. Yet only in his official correspondence. For instance, on 13 October 1808 he began a long series of letters to Baron von Platen in Sweden, and continued it for twenty years. Jessop's name is not mentioned in connection with the Caledonian Canal or any other activity, nor is his death remarked. Neither, however, is there reference to any other contemporary engineer of stature, except in one passing mention of Nimmo. Yet, as we noted in this book's Preface, he pays generous tribute to subordinates like Davidson.

So that the reader can make up his own mind upon Jessop's part in the canal's early history, I have summarised the main points:

(a) The idea and preliminary work was Telford's.
(b) The Commissioners appointed under the Act of 1803 themselves chose Jessop to give a second opinion.
(c) In late 1803 Jessop re-surveyed the line.
(d) Jessop alone signed the final report, and he alone made the estimate of construction cost excluding land.
(e) Jessop appeared alone before the Lords committee on the Bill of 1804 to prove the estimate; Telford on the estimate of land cost and other matters covered in the Bill's preamble. The com-

mittee's minutes refer to 'Mr William Jessop, Engineer' and 'Mr Thomas Telford, Surveyor'.

(f) A week earlier, Telford himself had asked for Jessop to give 'assistance and advice' in laying out the final line and had got it.

(g) Telford submitted to Jessop a list of resident staff he proposed to appoint, and their salaries. With some salary changes, Jessop agreed.

(h) Jessop and Telford (in that order) put final proposals to the Commissioners, and (in that order) received their formal Instructions, with an addendum for Telford on smaller practical matters.

(i) In Scotland with Telford, Jessop then issued 'Instructions' to John Telford, resident engineer at the Corpach end of the line, together with signed sectional drawings. These 'Instructions' are precise, stating in detail exactly how a canal should be staked and set out on virgin ground. They have survived in John Telford's notebook, but Jessop presumably gave another set to Matthew Davidson. If not, it would have been because he knew him so well already.

(j) The first report to the Commissioners, in late 1804, was drafted by Telford and sent to Jessop for examination and signature.

(k) Thereafter Jessop seems to have visited the works at least once a year, working together with Telford, who inspected them twice yearly, to settle problems. Each annual report was signed by both, Jessop's name coming first, until 1812, Jessop's last active year.

(l) In addition to the six sectional drawings, three signed and three others in similar style, from the notebook referred to earlier, more original Jessop drawings have been found, but none by Telford from the canal's early days. The presumption is, as would be reasonable for an engineer of Jessop's standing, that he did them himself. This assumption is borne out by the early lists of drawings left to the Institution of Civil Engineers by Telford[51]. The only full sets of drawings in these lists are for Fort Augustus locks, constructed after Jessop's death, and for the cast-iron gates adopted in 1813 after agreement with Jessop.

Jessop's position on the Caledonian was, however, rather different from that he held on such important canals as the Grand Junction, the Ellesmere or the Rochdale. In such cases he was principal engineer, finally responsible for design, estimates and performance, and working with one or more resident engineers, who in turn were served by subordinate engineers. On the Caledonian Hughes describes him correctly as 'senior engineer', Thomas Telford being his junior and, at the beginning, John Telford and Matthew Davidson as residents. Both were therefore responsible for all major decisions taken, and for everything written in the annual reports to the Commissioners. Nevertheless, it seems clear from the evidence we have that Jessop regarded himself as having ultimate responsibility because he was senior, and had much more reputation to lose should a major mistake be made.

To end this chapter let us glance at some contemporary comments on the mature Telford and the elderly Jessop, made by the Earl of Eglinton, leading promoter of the Glasgow, Paisley & Ardrossan Canal, and of Ardrossan Harbour[52]. He is writing to Alexander Mundell in London about Ardrossan harbour.

> 24 May 1808; 'Mr Telford I am aware will be very unwilling to give up his *own child*, the *Coffer dam*,★ and other nicknacks, I am therefore clear that we should employ some other Engineer, along with nautical men to have it clearly ascertained.'

> 5 June 1808: 'Mr Brown from Saltcoats with me . . . and we agree with you in thinking it will be proper to call in Mr Jessop and examine it along with Mr Telford.'

> 15 June 1808: 'As to Mr Jessop, I hope that as a subscriber that you will approve of what we have done in asking his assistance – Mr Telford, as I am informed is quite bigoted as to his own child – of the Coffer dammes which although I acknowledge to be ingenious enough, I consider perfectly trifling in comparison with the Noble harbour that will be made.'

> April 1810, copy letter (presumably from Lord Eglinton) to the Chancellor of the Exchequer: 'Mr Telford . . . has been employed by me and has had the superintendence of what has hitherto been carried on there, it was upon Mr Jessops report that the extension of the south pier was proposed.'†

★ Coffer dams, as an engineering device, date back to Roman times. Telford had used them without remark on his first Severn bridge at Montford.
† Presumably 'Report of William Jessop, Esq., Civil Engineer, on the Extension of the Pier at Adrossan', 18 July 1808. Printed in *Second Report of the Commissioners on Tidal Harbours*, Parl. Papers 1847, 32, 523. Jessop's MS report is in S.R.O. GO3141/18111.

9 Dec 1810, copy of a letter to Telford from Eglinton: 'when we conversed together upon the subject last time you were here, you appeared rather to wish that Mr Jessop should be upon the spot at the time you came to Ardrossan to fix it. This will be very agreeable to me, altho I have the highest opinion of your abilities Mr Jessop's concurrence will show at after times that I did not enter into the measure rashly, but on the opinion of two of the first Engineers in the Kingdom.'[53]

Telford's *Life* barely mentions Ardrossan harbour.

Chapter 7

The Caledonian Canal: from 1813 to Telford's Life

The canal was completed in 1822, its middle section shallower than the rest. A.D. Cameron's *The Caledonian Canal* gives an excellent account. I propose to study only the happenings of those years that are relevant to Jessop's reputation.

First of these is the dispute that later arose over leakage in and near Torvaine,* just above Inverness.

Neither Telford in his original, nor Rickman in his edited text, makes any special mention of the section. *The Civil Engineer*'s review of 1839 (see p. 180) notices the omission.

> Briefly, the canal line upwards from Muirtown had to be taken through a narrow space between the river Ness and Torvaine hill, formed of sand and gravel. To do so, the bed of the Ness was moved outwards to make room for a retaining wall and then the canal, before the steep slope of the hill was reached. Additionally, the width of the canal on this section was reduced. On its way the line had passed through clay beds, but no use was made of them for puddling. Instead, the canal past Torvaine was left unpuddled. When water was admitted, seemingly in 1816, it leaked badly, and the leakage went on increasing. Eventually, the length had to be puddled before it began to carry traffic in 1818. As a result, the section was now too small to be enlarged to its planned size.

What did happen? In his original report of 30 January 1804 Jessop had written that he had found the ground through which the canal was to be cut 'in its general appearance uncommonly favourable to the purpose', and that 'with a few Exceptions' trial bores and pits had confirmed this. He concluded that along most of the line the 'mixture of Gravel and Sand has a mixture of Earth among it sufficient to exclude Water' (i.e. that the bed would not need to be

* Sometimes spelt Torvean.

puddled with worked clay to make it watertight) except in a few places. The worst of these was 'the flat land at Inverness' which was mostly 'composed of Gravel and Sand'.

In Jessop's and Telford's *Third Report* written in November 1805, the engineers note that an additional expense will be the 'removing from the S.E. side of the River Ness, at Holme, the ground for the Embankment by which the River is turned at that place'. Later, the same report says: 'Where the River Ness runs close to the Base of Torvaine, ground has been cut from the Lands at Holme, and with it an Embankment has been formed to the River Ness, leaving a part of its Bed on the North side sufficient for the Canal'. Land on the opposite side, at Holme, was then cut away to restore the river's width.

On 12 October 1807 (*Fifth Report*), however, mention is made of a public road that is to be made between the canal and Torvaine. The ground removed from the hillside to make it would be used to raise banks at Bught. The *Seventh Report* says that 'We have determined the mode in which this Road shall be made and secured ... the experience of three years has now proved that the River Ness cannot injure the Canal Bank formed along the middle of its ancient Channel, opposite to Torvaine'.

The engineers' revised estimate for completing the canal, dated 10 October 1809, provides £2172 10s for 'Compleating Benching and Public Road along Torvaine'. However, a year later (October 1810, *Eighth Report*) they suggest that because 'the Sand and Gravel from the face of the Hill (i.e. Torvaine), if not cut away and removed, would for many years be liable to obstruct the Road', it might be less expensive to build it on Torvaine's north side. Plans and estimates were to be prepared by Matthew Davidson for the Commissioners, who were to decide. They in fact agreed. However, in the *Ninth Report*, they change their minds, and write:

On account of the Steepness of the Slope of Torraine Hill, and the tendency of the loose Sand and Gravel from it to obstruct the Road intended along the Bank of the Canal, it had been in contemplation to carry a road from Bught Bridge along the North side of that Hill, immediately under Dunain House, and through the Lands of Doughgarroch. But as the expense of carrying the Road in this direction, including necessary Fences, purchase of Land and damages, might perhaps exceed £.3,000, we have been led to reconsider the subject, and we think by reducing the bottom of the Canal in this place from Fifty to

Thirty Feet, and building a Retaining-Wall at the foot of the Slope, the loose ground liable to slip will be disposed of, and a sufficient space obtained for a safe and commodious Road, and this for less expense than in the other way, and also avoiding many difficulties which would probably arise in settling the value of Land and claims for compensation.

It may not be improper in this place to remark, that as the Canal will in general be sufficiently wide for large ships to pass each other, we venture to recommend that in the few places where there is very Deep Cutting, and no want of the Earth for Embankments, that the width be reduced to a Thirty feet bottom, as no material Inconvenience will attend it.

In the *Tenth Report* of October 1812, the last to be signed by Jessop, Torvaine is not mentioned, but when Telford alone reports in October 1813 (*Eleventh Report*) he tells us that after all the road was to run north of Torvaine. As it is now the A82, it was just as well.

The decision to change the road line back to the north must have been taken about the time the *Tenth Report* was written, for in the *Eleventh* it is

now in considerable state of forwardness, and will be completed during the ensuing summer. It will be more commodious than the old Road, and relieve the Canal from much inconvenience and future expense. As soon as the New Road has been opened to the Public, the Banking, Benching and Lining of that part of the Canal which passes along the Front of Torvaine, will be completed.

The word 'Lining' is elucidated by Telford's revised estimate of remaining expenses to be incurred to complete the canal: along the Bught stretch he refers to 'working in Lining in certain gravelly ground, and closing the opening in the Bank at present serving for the Public Road', and then 'Finishing Benching and Banks at Torvaine Hill . . .'

Telford's *Twelfth Report* is more enlightening:

Through the Lands of Kinmylies and Bught bottoming has been taken out to the proper depth, and the clay-lining levelled and worked upon the parts which consisted of open Gravel. The Benching along the steep face of Torvaine Hill has been completed, as far as adviseable until Water is brought into the Canal . . . From Torvaine, the Canal has been reported as completed.

And in his *Fourteenth Report* (October 1816) we reach the nub of the matter:

From these Locks* through the Lands of Muirtown, Kinmylies, Bught, Dunain, Doughgarroch and Doughfour, a distance of five Miles, the Canal has formerly been reported as having been completed to receive the Water; some part of this distance is through loose gravelly Land, which, although affording proper materials for substantial Banks when constructed with necessary puddle walls, has a bottom pervious to water, but as the Supply is superabundant, and the River acts as a tail drain adjacent to the lower Bank, for a great part of the distance to Doughfour, the mere loss of Water was considered immaterial; it was, therefore, during the construction of the Canal, judged more advise-able, to rely upon making the bottom in those parts water-tight by the cheap mode of introducing earthy matter and small Sand, carried by Boats after the Water was admitted, than by adopting the more expen-sive mode of lining with Clay. Accordingly as soon as the Water was introduced, the cheaper mode is now applying with the desired effect in all those parts where no private property intervenes between the Canal and the River; but in a portion of the Lands of Kinmylies and Bught, the Water threatening to be prejudicial to the adjacent valuable fields, before the aforesaid slow operation could be perfected, I have judged it advise-able, in the before-mentioned parts, to proceed by the more expensive mode of Lining; and as suitable materials are procured conveniently, measures have been taken to make these short portions perfectly water-tight, previously to the Canal being wanted for the purposes of Navi-gation.

When water was let into this section of the canal in 1816, the leakage was shown to be more serious, probably because it was in a section so near Inverness, and affecting lands owned by those who could complain effectively.

In October 1817 Telford wrote:

The Lining, which on account of the porous gravelly Soil through the Lands of Kinmylies and Bught, had been found unavoidable, has been carried on with great perseverance and effect, so as to admit eight feet of Water in the Canal; it is expected that by the time the Fort Augustus Works are recommenced in the Spring, that this Lining will be farther advanced, and enable the Vessels employed to carry their full loading; and that before the Middle District is in a state to admit larger Ships, the whole Lining will be completed; in one instance, near the old Bleach-

* Muirtown.

141

field, instead of proceeding by Lining, I have judged it preferable to increase the thickness of the lower Bank, by cutting from a convex bend of the upper Bank.

and a year later:

Through the Lands of Kinmylies and Bught, the Canal Lining having been carried to a height to admit ten feet of Water, (sufficient for the Vessels at present employed,) the Operations have been discontinued, in order that the Funds may be employed in the Middle District, to bring it with all practicable dispatch into a state to admit Coasting Vessels. The Bend at the old Bleachfield on Dunain Moor had been cut off, and Bank adjacent to the River Ness strengthened; the Banks from thence to the Regulating Lock remain in a perfect state.

Finally, he wrote at the end of September 1821 (*Nineteenth Report*)

The lining through the gravelly soil in the Lands of Kinmylies and Bught, has been raised so as to admit of nearly 13 feet water . . .

More trouble occurred in 1825 three years after the canal's opening at Dunaincroy above Torvaine towards Dochgarroch, where it proved impossible to maintain the then water depth of 15ft. Again the canal here had to be closed, and a huge patch of woollen cloth and puddle laid to a point 9ft up the banks: this cured the leakage.

We can now see that *The Civil Engineer*'s review was mistaken. The narrowing of the canal past Torvaine was due, firstly to a decision to build a main road alongside it, and then to a second, that no harm would result from narrowing at different points (*Ninth Report*).

As regards its accusation that the section should have been puddled early on, we can only reply that though Jessop had from the beginning noted that the worst section was 'the flat land at Inverness', nevertheless, both engineers had clearly decided not to puddle any of the canal bed, but only embankments and similar special cases. They were following a policy of 'wait and see', as happened on other canals also. When water was admitted to each section and the bed tested, leaks would show, and expensive action could then be taken where, and only where, it was needed. Reasonswould have been the canal's very tight annual expenditure allowance by government, and the ample supplies of water Scotland provides (one remembers Telford's original proposal for water-hungry turf-sided locks). Unfortunately for them, the worst leak-

Fig 23: The notorious Torvaine (Torvean) looking towards Inverness. Originally the river occupied the inner side of the curve. It was then narrowed on the outside by an embankment to make room for the canal and its embankment, and widened on the inner side in compensation. Torvaine hill rises above the canal, the A.82 road from Inverness behind it.

age showed up where it mattered most, on the outskirts of Inverness, where it flooded the provost's cellar. The search for a solution to make this stretch watertight was to go on for ten years.

Hughes in his *Memoir* is very tight-lipped, tries not to take sides, and decides that both engineers were to blame. But one can guess at his real feelings from this passage:

> ... there are many veterans of the profession still living, who, having been engaged on Jessop's great works in England and Ireland, have not ceased to regard him with a kind of religious awe, and who would point in triumph to many hundred miles of canal which he has successfully carried through great engineering difficulties, displaying superior skill in all the operations connected with earthwork, and ask, is it likely that he who has been so successful in works peculiarly and exclusively his own, could have perpetrated the blunders which some have ascribed to him on the Caledonian Canal?

This view is likely to be correct, given Jessop's wide experience as a drainage engineer, if indeed there were blunders at all, rather than the taking of calculated risks. With hindsight, the trouble does not seem severe in proportion to the length of the canal sections and the money saved by not laying long lengths of precautionary puddle, and later controversy therefore much out of proportion.

In my Preface I mentioned Robert Southey's tour of the canal in 1819 in company with Telford, and accompanied by Rickman. According to the latter's biographer, the opening of the canal in 1822 caused Rickman to take an initiative. 'Southey', writes Williams, 'fired by his tour in 1819, wrote three inscriptions, to be put up at Clachnaharry, Fort Augustus and Banavie respectively. These lines were carved on stone at Rickman's direction as a surprise for Telford'.[1]

They must have been. They are also somewhat of a surprise to us, given that Southey must have got his information from either Telford or Rickman. Here they are:

INSCRIPTIONS

FOR THE CALEDONIAN CANAL

1. AT CLACHNACHARRY.

ATHWART the island here, from sea to sea,
Between these mountain barriers, the Great Glen

Of Scotland offers to the traveller,
Through wilds impervious else, an easy path,
Along the shore of rivers and of lakes,
In line continuous, whence the waters flow
Dividing east and west. Thus had they held
For untold centuries their perpetual course
Unprofited, till in the Georgian age
This mighty work was plann'd, which should unite
The lakes, control the innavigable streams,
And through the bowels of the land deduce
A way, where vessels which must else have braved
The formidable Cape, and have essayed
The perils of the Hyperborean Sea,
Might from the Baltic to the Atlantic deep
Pass and repass at will. So when the storm
Careers abroad, may they securely here,
Through birchen groves, green fields, and pastoral hills,
Pursue their voyage home. Humanity
May boast this proud expenditure, begun
By Britain in a time of arduous war;
Through all the efforts and emergencies
Of that long strife continued, and achieved
After her triumph, even at the time
When national burdens bearing on the state
Were felt with heaviest pressure. Such expense
Is best economy. In growing wealth,
Comfort, and spreading industry, behold
The fruits immediate! And, in days to come,
Fitly shall this great British work be named
With whatsoe'er of most magnificence
For public use, Rome in her plenitude
Of power effected, or all-glorious Greece,
Or Egypt, mother-land of all the arts.

2. AT FORT AUGUSTUS

THOU who hast reach'd this level where the glede,
Wheeling between the mountains in mid air,
Eastward or westward as his gyre inclines,
Descries the German or the Atlantic sea,
Pause here; and, as thou seest the ship pursue

Her easy way serene, call thou to mind
By what exertions of victorious art
The way was open'd. Fourteen times upheaved,
The vessel hath ascended, since she changed
The salt sea water for the highland lymph;
As oft in imperceptible descent
Must, step by step, be lower'd before she woo
The ocean breeze again. Thou hast beheld
What basins, most capacious of their kind,
Enclose her, while the obedient element
Lifts or depones it burthen. Thou hast seen
The torrent hurrying from its native hills
Pass underneath the broad canal inhumed,
Then issue harmless thence; the rivulet
Admitted by its intake peaceably,
Forthwith by gentle overfall discharged;
And haply too thou hast observed the herds
Frequent their vaulted path, unconscious they
That the wide waters on the long low arch
Above them, lie sustained. What other works
Science, audacious in emprize, hath wrought,
Meet not the eye, but well may fill the mind,
Not from the bowels of the land alone,
From lake and steam hath their diluvial wreck
Been scoop'd to form this navigable way;
Huge rivers were controll'd, or from their course
Shoulder'd aside; and at the eastern mouth,
Where the salt ooze denied a resting place
There were the deep foundations laid, by weight
On weight immersed, and pile on pile down-driven,
Till steadfast as the everlasting rocks,
The massive outwork stands. Contemplate now
What days and nights of thought, what years of toil,
What inexhaustive springs of public wealth
The vast design required; the immediate good,
The future benefit progressive still;
And thou wilt pay thy tribute of due praise
To those whose counsels, whose decrees, Whose care,
For after ages formed the generous work.

3. AT BANAVIE

WHERE these capacious basins, by the laws
Of the subjacent element receive
The ship, descending or upraised, eight times,
From stage to stage with unfelt agency
Translated; fitliest may the marble here
Record the Architect's immortal name.
Telford it was, by whose presiding mind
The whole great work was plann'd and perfected;
Telford, who o'er the vale of Cambrian Dee,
Aloft in air, at giddy height upborne,
Carried his navigable road, and hung
High o'er Menai's straits the bending bridge;
Structures of more ambitious enterprise
Than minstrels in the age of old romance
To their own Merlin's magic lore ascribed.
Nor hath he for his native land perform'd
Less in this proud design; and where his piers
Around her coast from many a fisher's creek
Unshelter'd else, and many an ample port,
Repel the assailing storm; and where his roads
In beautiful and sinuous line far seen,
Wind with the vale, and win the long ascent,
Now o'er the deep morass sustain'd, and now
Across ravine, or glen, or estuary,
Opening a passage through the wilds subdued.

In considering them, let us remember that once the war had ended, in 1815, the main naval purpose of the canal ended too; remember also that, as A. D. Cameron writes[2] 'There is no doubt that Telford missed the expert advice of Jessop after 1812, and no one was appointed to replace him'. Yet now Telford was only to spare the canal one 6-week visit a year from his many other works. Troubles multiplied: an estimate made in 1816 for completion in three years became six – and then less complete; estimates of income from tolls had been wildly optimistic, and of money still needed, not nearly enough. These were not the kind of mistakes Jessop made; nor were some others listed in Cameron's Chapter 9. Not everything would have gone right; but I suspect it would have gone a good deal less wrong – but that is what twelve years of additional experience does for one. Therefore when opening did take place, the atmosphere was not one of congratulation. Telford was not even there; presumably he was keeping his head down.

So Southey's verses were, in 1822, out of tune with the occasion. In the Clachnaharry poem, not many would then have agreed with 'Such expense is best economy' while in that destined for Fort Augustus the words 'Contemplate now. . . . What inexhaustive springs of public wealth the vast design required' would have found only too many unintended echoes.

The oddest poem is that meant for Banavie, for we know that, unlike Fort Augustus, the Banavie staircase had been designed and built (except for the lock gates) in Jessop's time. Yet here we have the flat statement:

> . . . fitliest may the marble here
> Record the Architect's immortal name.
> Telford it was, by whose presiding mind
> The whole great work was plann'd and perfected

Southey then goes on, irrelevantly in the light of the other straight-forward inscriptions, to add a description of Pontcysyllte:

> Telford, who o'er the vale of Cambrian Dee
> Aloft in air, at giddy height upborne,
> Carried his navigable road . . .

The *dénouement* was also odd. Only one inscription, that intended for Banavie, was chosen to be engraved on marble, whether because it was most laudatory or because, unlike the other two, it did not mention the canal's cost, we don't know. Neither do we know who paid for it. Williams implies that Rickman did, but the *Inverness Courier* for 24 October 1922, reporting the canal's centenary, says:

> The story has been handed down that the tablet was subscribed for by the various engineers engaged in constructing the canal, who desired that it should be erected to Telford's honour at the opening. With characteristic modesty, however, the eminent engineer desired it put out of sight . . .

Thus, having been engraved with the word TELFORD in capitals, it was never erected, but remained forgotten until 1922, when it was erected, not at Banavie, but at Clachnaharry, for which site the opening lines are inapposite.

In 1824 a supplement was published to bring up to date the fourth, fifth and sixth editions of the *Encyclopaedia Britannica*. The article on the Caledonian Canal seems to have been written soon after 1816, the last date mentioned. It is signed H. H. (although written by, in fact, Robert Stevenson) and shows the author to be well acquainted with the line. His account reveals clear appreciation of Jessop's part: his calling in to re-survey; his responsibility for the estimate; the joint Jessop–Telford report that followed; the joint visit in 1804 to lay out the line; and the joint fixing of wages in 1804.

When the author describes the canal's route, he is struck by the pre-consolidation technique used at the sea-lock at Clachnaharry, and refers to its introduction by 'Messrs Jessop and Telford'. He goes on to describe the successfully built lock as 'perhaps, the most extraordinary work upon the whole line of this navigation, or, indeed, in any part of the Kingdom . . .' H.H. is much struck by the size, weight, and efficiency of the cast-iron gates, but attributes no credit; when he gets to the regulating lock of Loch Lochy, he notes that 'the hollow quoins . . . are actually constructed of cast-iron, being a new application of that British manufacture in massive building'. At Banavie, he confirms that 'This majestic chain of locks was finished, excepting the gates, in 1811, and describes the whole as 'presenting the greatest mass of masonry any where to be found as applicable to the purposes of a canal' – I would think a very accurate statement for its date.

In all, it is an unexceptionable account.

In 1818 Charles Dupin, marine engineer and traveller, published in Paris his *Memoirs sur la Marine et Les Ponts et Chaussées* de France et d'Angleterre*, which contained special sections on Plymouth breakwater and the Caledonian Canal. Telford's own copy† is inscribed 'to his most estimated friend Mr Telford' by 'Ch. Dupin'. The book was issued in English in 1819 as *Two Excursions to the Ports of England, Scotland and Ireland, in 1816, 1817, and 1818; with a description of the breakwater at Plymouth, and of the Caledonian Canal.*

Dupin refers to Telford's original survey of the Highlands and report of 1803. He then goes on:

The Committee, appointed by Parliament . . . examined Mr. Telford's

---

* Ponts et Chaussées as used here may roughly be translated as 'public works'.

† In the Institution of Civil Engineers Library.

plan; and in order to ascertain still more positively and practicability of its execution, as well as the probable expense of the intended canal, they called before them Messrs Jessop (since dead) and Rennie, two of the most eminent civil engineers at that time in England . . .

The Committee . . . recommended, in their Report, the execution of the plan proposed by Mr Telford. In consequence, a Bill was brought into Parliament, in . . . 1803 . . . By the act . . . a Board of Commissioners was nominated . . . who immediately appointed Mr. Thomas Telford to be their engineer, and ordered him to make again an entire survey of the whole line . . . Mr. Jessop was likewise charged to inspect the whole line and to add thereto his particular estimates, with a view of furnishing to the Commissioners, in this manner, a double certainty in regard to the operations to be undertaken.

Thereafter Dupin's detailed description of the canal does not again mention Jessop's name, and it makes one significant mistake, when it says of Banavie that 'This majestic chain of locks was finished, with the exception of the gates, in 1817'. As we know, the flight, except for the gates, was completed in 1811 during the Jessop period. Given Dupin's inscription in a surviving copy of the French edition to 'his most estimated friend Mr. Telford', the source of his information seems clear, even though he mentions Stevenson, and has presumably read his then unpublished account. The removal of Jessop's name from the Caledonian's history had begun.

Dupin's Caledonian section was reissued in Vol II of his *Force Commerciale de La Grande-Bretagne*, published in Paris in 1824 and in translation as *The Commercial Power of Great Britain* in 1825. Between 1818 and 1825 Dupin had become, among others, an honorary member of the Royal Society of Edinburgh and of the Institution of Civil Engineers. The text is only slightly different. Jessop is still not mentioned, though the sentence about Banavie locks quoted above has been removed. A final paragraph recording the canal's opening in 1822 had been added.

One year after Dupin, J. Dutens also published in Paris his *Memoirs sur les Travaux Publics de l'Angleterre*. Whereas Dupin was an interested and well-informed traveller, Dutens went more thoroughly into his subject, seemingly also having had access to Stevenson's work. He gives an excellent detailed account of the canal. The embankment and pre-consolidation technique used at Clachnaharry he attributes to 'MM. Jessop et Telford', and goes on to call the sea-lock and embankment there 'peut-être l'ouvrage le plus extraordinaire de toute la ligne du canal et même du royaume'.* The work at Torvaine and its neighbourhood is described, but not in any critical sense, and so to Banavie locks, 'Cette chaine majestueuse', which, except for the gates, was 'terminée en 1811'.† Later Dutens writes of 'cette grande masse de constructions, peut-être la plus considerable qui se voie sur aucun canal'; this from a Frenchman who knew well Riquet's great earlier staircase at Fonserannes (Béziers) on the Canal du Midi. For the moment Jessop had been reinstated.

Stéphane Flachat's book, *Histoire des Travaux et de l'Aménagement des Eaux du Canal Caledonien*, with maps and delightful illustrations, was published in Paris in 1828. It is described as 'Rédigée d'après les rapports de MM. Jessop et Telford, Ingénieurs – Directeurs . . .' Flachat was a sound man. He did his paperwork on the canal reports, visited the canal after its completion and once met Telford. Flachat's and Stevenson's are the best accounts of the Caledonian written before the publication of Telford's *Life*.

He gets Jessop in his right place early on; 'M. Jessop, l'un des ingénieurs les plus célèbres de l'Angleterre, chargé, par les commissaires du canal Calédonien, de suivre les travaux de ce canal concurrement avec M. Telford . . .'‡

As regards Torvaine and other tender spots, Flachat, himself especially concerned with hydraulic matters, makes it clear that the engineers had deliberately followed a policy of 'wait and see' as regards leakages. They did not arise, naturally, until after Jessop's time, when canal sections were filled with water. The first stage was then to inject sand into the over-light soil to fill the cavities. Usually that sufficed. If not, then the classic but expensive remedy of puddling was used. He implies no blame, and a modern reader cannot but agree, given the overriding need for economy. Neither Flachat's nor Duten's book was published in Britain. Dupin's was.

Early in Henry Meikle's general article, 'Navigation Inland', in the *Britannica*'s 7th edition (1830–42), he refers to the 'new surveys . . . made by Messrs Jessop and Telford', but describes the work as

* 'perhaps the most extraordinary work of the whole canal or even the kingdom', a sentence seemingly derived from Stevenson.
† 'This majestic chain . . . completed in 1811 . . . this mass of building, perhaps the most considerable to be found on any canal'. This reference may have caused Dupin to amend his earlier text.
‡ 'Mr. Jessop, one of the most eminent English engineers, was ordered by the Caledonian Canal Commissioners to execute the canal works concurrently with Mr Telford . . .'

'under the direction of Mr Telford', and goes on to mention the canal's finally-decided dimensions as 'proposed by him [Telford]', which we know is not quite the case. The rest of Meikle's low-key account does not mention either engineer.

Let us now move to Telford's *Life*.

Chapter 8

The Caledonian Canal: Telford's Life and Jessop's Lessening

The first version of the *Life* is again entirely in Telford's handwriting. It begins, as does the printed text, with a description of the Great Glen, due credit being given to 'the justly celebrated' James Watt's employment in 1773 to survey and report upon such a line. He goes on to his own employment to survey it again for a canal, as one of several possible projects. At this point (footnote to printed p.51) he suggests what was to become Appendix B of the printed text, his report of 15 March 1803 recommending a canal.

Where the sixth line of p.52 of the printed text of the *Life* refers readers to 'Appendix (C), List of Commissioners', Telford originally wrote out his proposed appendices, as follows:

In Appendix
Names of Commissioners
Instructions from the Secretary, J. Rickman, dated 6 August. 1803*
William Jessop associated 2 Feby 1804†
Two Instructions from Secretary 18 June 1804‡
Messrs Telford & Jessops Letters do§
Prices of Labour fixed by W. J. & T. T. 29 Nov. 1804¶
Official Return of Vessels & Cargoes Report 1807 – with Secretary's Observations.

Here, then, Telford is correctly setting out the evidence for what actually occurred, insofar as he, Telford, was concerned, though the vital fact that it was Jessop's estimate of construction cost and Jessop's evidence to the Parliamentary committee upon it that enabled the Bill's acceptance is omitted.

* An extract is quoted in the centre of p. 155 of *WJE*.
† See foot of p.157 *WJE*.
‡ See p.160 *WJE*.
§ In fact, Telford's letter to Jessop is dated 8 June, Jessop's reply 18 June.
¶ Note the order of the initials here.

Having described the terrain, Telford goes on to the canal as built, and then lists three locks or systems as worthy of special description, the sea-locks at Clachnaharry and Corpach, and the staircase at Fort Augustus.

When he writes of Clachnaharry sea-lock and the preconsolidation technique that was used (see p. 128) he says: '... after much consideration it therefore became necessary to adopt a method that I had not before known to be practised ...' *prima facie* suggesting that he had learned of it from Jessop. He goes on to mention the types of stone used for construction, the types of lock gate (and here occurs an incidental mention of Jessop's name in the text: 'for the Eastern district, the Iron work, Heads, Heels and Bars, were cast and fitted at Messrs Jessop's Works* at Butterley in Derbyshire ...') and various technical points.

He ends with something of an apology – unnecessary, I should have thought – for the time taken upon construction, and for the increase over estimate in its cost. He writes:

> 'I have by two Papers in the Appendix [See Appendix Reports 1814 and 1818] explained why the construction of this great Work has occupied so many Years, and also, nominally, cost nearly double what it was originally Estimated at.' He instances the increases in wages and the cost of materials due to the long war, while the annual sums made available by Parliament remained the same; the Appendices he chose would have made his point.

His manuscript now peters out in a description of the difficult winds to be found in the Great Glen, and a statement that 'for 7 years this Navigation has been used at all seasons without accident – Steam Boats, and even Sailing Vessels have passed from Sea to Sea in 24 Hours.'

The whole account of the Caledonian Canal is curiously dead and without breadth or depth: only in his description of lock engineering does it come alive because he is interested in the ways by which practical difficulties were overcome.

Telford's second draft, though mainly in his own still firm handwriting, also carries Rickman's interpolations, mostly of a sensible editorial kind.

This version follows the first in its description of the Great Glen,

---

* A curious mistake, for the firm was known as B. Outram & Co until it became The Butterley Company.

and of his own first employment. Again he suggests what was to become Appendix B, his own Report of 15 March 1803. But this time his other proposed appendices, which included evidence of Jessop's participation, are completely omitted.

He again describes the canal as built, and again chooses locks or lock systems worthy of special attention. This time, however, instead of three, Clachnaharry, Corpach and Fort Augustus, is added in Rickman's handwriting 'and 4th, for magnitude of fabrick, the Connected Locks abovementioned' i.e. Banavie. This interpolation is then copied by Telford into his own text as 'and 4th, for magnitude of fabrick, the beforementioned 8 connected Locks'. It seem clear, therefore, that Telford had left out the Banavie staircase from his special list, perhaps because he knew that credit lay with Jessop as well as himself, and that Rickman persuaded him to include it.*

Now comes Rickman, in his own handwriting, to insert the whole passage about the history of locks later to be printed on pp 56–8, beginning at 'the facilities of inland navigation' at line 19 of p.56 right through to 'that extensive empire' at line 16 of p.58. The passage appears to have been inserted with Telford's consent, for the page number where it is to be placed seems to be in his handwriting.

Then follow, as before, descriptions of the problems set by Clachnaharry, Corpach and Fort Augustus. When we come to Telford's original wording: '. . . it therefore became necessary to adopt a method that I had not before known to be practised', has become 'it became necessary to adopt a *new method, one at least* which I had not known *to have been practised*', the italicised words being in Rickman's writing. The sense is therefore altered to suggest that Telford invented the technique.†

We now turn to the printed text, which generally follows the

---

* It is interesting that Robert Southey (*Journal of a Tour of Scotland in 1819*), when taken to Banavie by Telford and Rickman, is greatly struck by what he saw – and rightly; '. . . the greatest piece of such masonry in the world, and the greatest work of its kind, beyond all comparison.' Yet nowhere does he give special credit to any named person. As we saw, he changed his mind in retrospect.

† Robert Southey, an accurate recorder, describes Clachnaharry and the pre-consolidation technique used. He goes on (p.168): 'This was a conception of Telford's, and had it not been for this bold thought the design of the canal must have been abandoned'. He was travelling in company with Telford and Rickman, and must have got his information from one or the other.

second version through the Great Glen to the description of the canal line. When the Banavie staircase is mentioned, we now find a footnote, presumably Rickman's, which draws attention to it as 'quite unparalleled in canal operations', and mentions that it was finished in 1819. Strictly, this is correct, though the *Ninth Report to the Commissioners*, dated October 1811 and signed by Jessop and Telford, says: 'The Masonry of "Neptune's Staircase" (if we may be permitted to use the appellation applied by the Workmen to the Chain of Locks on Corpach Moss) is completed'. Therefore the main constructional work had been finished while Jessop was still senior engineer.

After Telford has described the building of the Fort Augustus locks, he writes a new paragraph:

> 'These three Locks* being instances of extreme cases on a large Scale I considered it my duty to record, much in detail, all the means employed in each case, in hope they may prove useful to practical Engineers, but from long experience, that altho' the principal Engineer decided upon the most adviseable, yet then much depends upon judicious Workmen . . .'

after which follow tributes to Simpson, Cargill and Wilson.

Telford's words are difficult to read because of heavy erasures. They become, I judge,

> These three Locks being an extreme case of conflict with surrounding water, I here considered it my duty to record, much in detail, all the means employed in hope that such particular descriptions may prove useful to practical Engineers, and also to show from experience that altho' the principal Engineer has decided upon the most advisable outline of operations very much depends upon the workmanship and attention . . .'

Here Rickman seems to be tightening what Telford wrote in order to make it more personal to him. However, the passage then disappeared from the printed text, leaving only:

> The Caledonian Canal locks are not only constructed on an unusually large scale, but, in consequence of localities, they afford useful information to the practical engineer . . .

He ends with this paragraph:

> Thus in the course of 20 Years, this great and difficult Work performed

* He seems to mean 'sets of locks'.

in a remote Country, under a variety of disadvantages, is evidence of what may be accomplished by judicious arrangement and steady perseverance, under enlightened Commissioners, with the assistance of an able and upright Secretary.

In the printed version, however, this passage, slightly amended, ends at 'perseverance'. One can guess why.

For the appendices, it seems that Rickman is responsible. Of those suggested by Telford in his first draft, only one is left, (B), his report of 15 March 1803 upon the practicability of a canal (see p. 115). Appendix (C) of the printed version gives the 'Report from the Committee on Mr Telford's Survey of the Highlands of Scotland – 14th June 1803' but adds a list of Commissioners, those given in the 1803 Act, but also (not in the Act), 'John Rickman, Secretary, Thomas Telford, Engineer and James Hope, Law Agent at Edinburgh'. Upon this survey the government acted. In the course of it, Jessop's name appears along with Telford and Rennie as one of the expert witnesses.

There follows the quotation in full of the last three paragraphs of Appendix (C):

Your Committee are therefore deeply impressed with the immediate necessity of employing the people of the country in the execution of this great national work; which will excite a spirit and introduce habits of industry, and will most probably check the present rage for emigration, and prevent its future progress.

Your Committee are equally convinced of the practicability, as of the importance, of this work. The strata under ground along the line of the canal have not yet been proved, by sinking pits or boring; but from the general appearance of the soil near the surface, there is no reason to suppose that there is any rock near the surface of the ground in the line of the canal; and from estimates, which have been made under this supposition, it appears to the Committee, as far as they can depend upon Mr Telford's knowledge of local circumstances, stated in his Report, that, exclusively of the value of land, which, except near Inverness, is in general of inferior quality, the execution of the works, in a very plain though substantial manner, with the materials to be found in the country, and with the advantage to be derived from the superabundant supplies of water on the summit level, which will enable the engineer to introduce a new and very economical mode of forming the locks★ that the whole expense of a canal to contain twenty feet depth, would not exceed three hundred and fifty thousand pounds. It appears, however,

★ Telford proposed turfsided locks.

to the Committee, from Mr Jessop's mode of calculation, that his estimate would amount to four hundred and seventy-eight thousand five hundred pounds, but he estimates each lock at ten thousand pounds, whereas Mr. Telford calculates the twenty-five locks at five instead of ten thousand pounds each; which excess of estimate beyond Mr Telford's is therefore accounted for within the sum of three thousand two hundred pounds, by the difference of the expense of twenty-five locks. – Mr Rennie supposes that the proposed canal would cost from six to seven hundred thousand pounds; but your Committee beg leave to observe, that neither Mr. Jessop nor Mr. Rennie are acquainted, from their personal observations, with any local circumstances, they not ever having made a survey, nor having ever been upon the line of the canal; but form their judgment from their experience of other works.

Your Committee, from a full consideration of all the evidence laid before them, and annexed to this Report by way of Appendix, submit to the House their opinion, That the execution of the inland navigation, proposed in Mr. Telford's survey, under all due regulations for the economical expenditure of such monies as may be employed in this great work, will be a measure highly conducive to the prosperity and happiness of that part of Scotland in which it is situated, and of great importance to the general interests of the whole United Kingdom.

This extract ingeniously presents Jessop in a bad light. The reader will not realise that it was Jessop's estimate of lock costs that was preferred either to Telford's or Rennie's, and in fact formed the basis of the final estimate upon which the Bill proceeded. Nor, having read the pejorative sentence: 'neither Mr. Jessop nor Mr. Rennie are acquainted, from their personal observations, with any local circumstances, they not having ever made a survey, nor having ever been upon the line of the canal', that Jessop was within two months to be asked officially for his 'opinion and assistance'.

Then follows Appendix D, 'Construction of the Sea-Lock at Corpach', a technical account which names neither engineer. No corresponding section on Clachnaharry is included.

When Telford has finished his description of the canal, his first draft goes on:

I have by two Papers in the Appendix explained why the construction of this great Work has occupied so many Years, and also, nominally, cost nearly double what it was originally Estimated at . . .'

In the margin he has noted 'See Appendix Reports 1814 and 1818.' The printed text omits both of these (which refer to periods when

Telford was in sole charge), but instead includes Appendix (D), which describes the construction of the sea-lock at Corpach, and (E), 'Comparative Prices of Materials and Rate of Wages in 1803, compared with 1814, on the Caledonian Canal' (i.e. from the canal's initiation to the year of Jessop's death). Clearly Telford, quite rightly, wished his explanation to cover most of the time the canal took to build, and so quoted the later reports, whereas the substituted Appendix does not.

We can perhaps conclude that Telford's original account in his first draft was biased in his own favour, but not obtrusively so; though he should surely have mentioned Jessop at key points in his text, he did establish Jessop's original status in his proposed Appendices. We do not know whether they were left out of his second draft at his own initiative, or at Rickman's suggestion. But the rest of the substantial changes made must have been Rickman's. The result was to produce in the printed version, titled as 'written by himself', an account that avoids any description of the Parliamentary processes that produced the canal, or of the vitally important early steps that have been described in Chapter 6, and which, as in the Banavie or Clachnaharry preconsolidation interpolations, nudges the reader away from the part played by Jessop. The printed text and its appendices therefore emerge as a considerable exercise in *suppressio veri*, with the inclusion, seemingly without Telford's initiative, of Appendix C as intended *suggestio falsi*.

Finally, we may note that during the period when Telford was working with Jessop on the Caledonian Canal, in 1805–12[1] he was also acting as engineer for the Aberdeen harbour improvements, with Jessop as his consultant. Though the work is well covered in the *Life*, Jessop is nowhere mentioned.

Let us now follow the influence upon history of the publication of the *Life*.

The eighth edition of the *Encyclopaedia Britannica* (1852–60)[2] describes the Great North Holland Canal[3], then goes on to say that 'our own country furnishes us with a similar work of great magnitude and boldness; we allude to the Caledonian Canal, originally projected by Watt and Jessop, and ultimately executed by Telford'. Here we part company with exactitude. Telford's not Jessop's name should follow Watt's as projecting the canal, but Jessop's should be added to Telford's as executing it. Then in the ninth edition (1875–89) Watt's name is followed by Telford's alone, as originating the Caledonian line. Then follows: 'In carrying out this remarkable work Telford had to deal with difficulties of no ordinary kind ... The work ... is a noble monument of his engineering skill'. Thus between the early 1850s and the early 1870s Jessop's name fades from ordinary accounts of the canal. Here are some examples. Priestley in 1831[4] says that Telford examined the canal's line, and recommended a canal of stated dimensions. He goes on, 'the estimate formed by Mr W. Jessop, according to these dimensions, amounted to' etc. He continues carefully but correctly, 'The whole of the works on this line of canal are of the first order, and exhibit the combined skill of the excellent engineers, who were entrusted with its execution ...'

Samuel Smiles in his very brief notice of Jessop's life[5], says 'He was also employed as engineer for the Caledonian Canal, in which he was succeeded by Telford, who carried out the work'. This implication that Jessop was only concerned with the canal's initiation is carried on into Smiles' description, in his biography of Telford, of the Caledonian. He writes (p.411)

Mr Telford's first inspection of the district was made in 1801, and his report was sent in to the Treasury in the course of the following year ... A board of commissioners was eventually appointed to carry out the formation of the canal. Mr. Telford, on being appointed principal engineer of the undertaking, was requested at once to proceed to Scotland and prepare the necessary working survey. He was accompanied on the occasion by Mr. Jessop as consulting engineer. Twenty thousand pounds were granted ... and the works were commenced, in the beginning of 1804, by the formation of a dock or basin adjoining the intended tide-lock at Corpach, near Bannavie.

Jessop's name does not occur again, and the only authority quoted by Smiles is the *Life*.

Smiles, unlike later biographers, does bring Jessop in at the beginning of the enterprise, but makes the fundamental mistake of thinking that Telford had been appointed principal, and Jessop consulting, engineer. Therefore he assumes that after the original survey, Jessop dropped out. This is natural, as the only authority quoted for constructional details is the *Life*.

David Stevenson, in *The Principles and Practice of Canal and River Engineering*, 2nd ed, 1872, after referring to Telford's original report, writes, however, 'In carrying out this remarkable work Telford had to deal with difficulties of no ordinary kind ... The work ... is a noble monument of his engineering skill'.* An interesting point here is that Stevenson's Preface tells us that 'Some of the information contained in the following chapters was published as the article 'Inland Navigation' in the eighth edition of the *Encyclopaedia Britannica*'. I have quoted earlier from that article, which mentions Jessop. Now, within the same period, his name has gone.

Why? Maybe a clue can be found in L. F. Vernon-Harcourt's work. In 1882 was published the first edition of his *Treatise on Rivers and Canals*. His account describes the canal's course, refers to Telford's original survey, and states: 'Telford was entrusted with the carrying out of the work ...' The only source quoted is the *Life*. The *Life* was published in 1838, and my experience is that it takes some ten to fifteen years for published information to make its way into reference books. It therefore seems likely that the disappearance of Jessop's name from the *Britannica* after the early fifties, and its non-appearance in David Stevenson in 1872 and Vernon-Harcourt in 1882, is due to statements made in the *Life*.

As with the Ellesmere Canal, I have quoted few recent biographers and historians; their works can be consulted easily enough. Let us end this account of Jessop's involvement in the building of the Caledonian Canal with the current navigation authority. The British Waterways Board is firmly traditional in its publicity material; 'The canal was engineered by a famous Scotsman, Thomas Telford ...'

* These words are taken *verbatim* from the *Encyclopaedia Britannica*'s ninth edition.

Chapter 9

The Societies and the Institution

By about 1760 British industrial enterprises had begun to develop in size and complexity. They began to need better transport by road or the new canals and to require water or the new steam power. Those who built and serviced them changed from being millwrights and mechanics to become the founders of a new profession, that of non-military engineers engaged in what we would now call civil and mechanical engineering. Most, because of their employment in large-scale enterprises, became increasingly involved in Parliamentary business as servants of promoters or opponents e.g. of new inland waterways, and so found themselves in London while Parliament was sitting.

With so much in common, it seemed sensible that they should organise regular meetings. The main objective would have been social; to pass pleasant evenings with like-minded colleagues, though when such colleagues do meet, ideas are exchanged, news brought up to date and useful words can be dropped into receptive ears.

So, on 15 March 1771, at the King's Head Tavern, Holborn, John Smeaton and six others met. With the veteran Thomas Yeoman in the chair, it was

> 'Agreed that the Civil Engineers of this Kingdom do form themselves into a Society ... who shall meet once a fortnight ... at seven o'clock from Christmas or so soon as any of the country Members come to Town ... to the end of the sitting of the Parliament.'

On the cover of the book Yeoman bought for the minutes appear the words 'An. 1771. Society of Civil Engineers'. Earlier uses of the phrase have been found, but now the words 'civil engineer' became known. Between 1771 and 1800, 42 members had been listed. John

162

Smeaton, greatest engineer of his day, had approved the Society's formation and attended its meetings regularly, and long after his death it was renamed, in compliment to him, The Smeatonian Society of Civil Engineers.

William Jessop, pupil and later assistant to Smeaton until 1772, still under 30, was in 1773 elected a member, and in 1774 became the Society's first secretary. He remained so till 1792; and in 1793 was a member of one committee for reorganising the Society and of another for the publication of Smeaton's *Reports*. He remained a member until his death in 1814.

John Rennie, four years younger than Telford, was elected in 1785 aged only 24, a tribute to brilliance that showed so early. Later he joined Jessop on the committee for reorganising the Society and for the publication of Smeaton's *Reports*, and after the older man's death became its dominant figure.[1]

Telford was never a member. In a discussion that followed a paper by Professor A. W. Skempton upon 'Early Members of the Smeatonian Society', Skempton observed that 'His conspicuous absence may reflect a mutual coolness, as Rennie was the dominant figure in the Society from about 1805 to 1821. But it may be that Telford simply did not choose to be a member; Jessop would surely have asked him if he wanted to join, while they were working together on the Ellesmere Canal'.[2] Given the situation I have outlined in this book, it seems unlikely that Telford would have wanted to join a Society of which Jessop was so senior a member.

As regards John Rennie, L.T.C. Rolt, in his *Thomas Telford*, (pp148–9) quotes a letter★ of April 1805 from Telford to James Watt referring to the death of Rennie's wife:

I am truly sorry to find that Mr Rennie has suffered so serious and distressing a loss, and I am also sorry to inform you that his conduct prevents me from benefiting by his acquaintance. Altho' I never had any connection with him in business or ever intentionally did anything to injure or interfere with him, I, in every quarter, hear of his treating my character with a degree of illiberality not very becoming. This is so marked a part of his conduct, that I really believe it does him a serious injury and proves serviceable to me. As I am desirous of not suffering in your good opinion, I mention this with a view to counteracting any insinuations which may be advanced to my disadvantage.

★ I have checked Rolt's quotation against the original, which is dated 5 April 1805 from Chester, and have made a few minor emendations to Rolt's text as a result.

The quarrel was still going strong five years later when, seemingly in April 1810, the Earl of Eglinton wrote to the Chancellor of the Exchequer: '. . . Mr. Rennie I am informed is on the worst terms with Mr Telford . . .'[3]

Rolt speculates that the cause of Rennie's dislike of Telford may have been professional jealousy. This may indeed have been so, but surely the wording of the Eglinton quotation and the length of the quarrel suggest that there was also a much more personal reason?

Both Smeatonians from 1785, by the early 1790s Rennie and Jessop were professionally associated in circumstances that could well have put the younger man at enmity with the elder.[*] Indeed, there were occasions when each considered the other wrong, and said so. After Rennie had lost two Bills to construct the Rochdale Canal, Jessop had been called in to make new proposals for water supply, and then to pilot the third, successful, Bill of 1794 through Parliament, thenceforward remaining as principal engineer[4]. Almost at the same time Rennie had successfully taken the Kennet & Avon Bill through Parliament, only to have Jessop called in to revise the line – a revision that removed Rennie's proposed long summit tunnel[5]. On the other hand, Rennie was right on the Misterton drainage[6], and on Blisworth tunnel[7]. Yet Samuel Hughes[8] says that 'the great Rennie was introduced to the engineership of the Lancaster Canal, on the recommendation of and by the advice of Mr. Jessop', and *William Jessop, Engineer* lists numerous instances of collaboration by the two engineers over the period to 1805. In one case, the Somersetshire Coal Canal, correspondence shows them as good friends. Professional differences, therefore, do not preclude personal friendship.

I have tried unsuccessfully to find evidence of the quarrel's origin. In its absence, is it not therefore a fair assumption that the second engineer of the canal mania did not at all like the way his friend, and to some degree his mentor, Jessop, had been treated by Telford on the Ellesmere Canal? Rennie dominated the Smeatonians until his death in 1821. Can we not therefore loosely link the

---

* The table on p.262 of *William Jessop, Engineer*, shows that during the canal mania of 1789–1796 Jessop was by far the leading engineer with 27 appearances before House of Lords committees on canal and navigation Bills; Rennie comes next with 16, followed by Robert Whitworth with 7. Telford appeared only once.

fact that Telford never became a Smeatonian with Rennie's dislike of him?

In this book's *Preface* another possibility emerges, that Telford was one who did not feel comfortable in the public company of equals or superiors in his own profession, though happy to have a band of devoted subordinates. If this characteristic underlay his whole life, as I believe it did, then it seems likely that he would not have enjoyed mixing with his peers in the relaxed atmosphere of the Smeatonian Society. But when he was offered an opportunity to head his own group, then he found a place where he could belong and yet be happy.

In 1817, when Telford was 60, it was his 23-year-old assistant Henry R. Palmer who called five other engineers to a meeting, on 2 January 1818 of what was then called the Institution of Civil Engineers for Facilitating the Acquirement of Knowledge Necessary in their Profession and for Promoting Mechanical Philosophy. He had rightly identified a real need. In his address, he spoke of the lack of means available to anyone wishing to be a civil engineer regarding instruction in the science and practice of engineering, and the need for an organisation which would address their deficiencies; aims and objectives which, then clearly laid down, have remained to this day. Yet the feeling of this small group of pioneers was not immediately shared, for only four more joined them in the first two years, one, William Provis, a Telford associate.

Then on 25 January 1820, with Palmer in the chair, Provis moved

> That in order to give effect to the principle of the institution, and to render its advantages more general, both to the members and the country at large, it is expedient to extend its provisions by the election of a President, whose extensive practice as a civil engineer has gained him the first-rate celebrity; and of persons as honorary members or associates, who, by their indefatigable exertions in the cause of science, have rendered themselves respected for their learning.
>
> *Resolved*, That a respectful communication be made to Thomas Telford, Esq., F.R.S.E., Civil Engineer, requesting him to patronize this institution, by taking on himself the office of President to the same.

Telford accepted, and in the course of his inaugural address on 21 March 1821, said in words that were later quoted in the *Life*:

> Having had no share in, or even knowledge of, the original formation of this institution, I can speak with more freedom of its merits. It has, in

165

truth, like other valuable establishments of our happy country, arisen from the wants of its society, and, being the result of its present state, promises to be both useful and lasting.

From a view of the topography and statistics of this country, it is quite evident that civil engineering has increased to an extent and importance which urgently demand such a separate establishment as you, its earliest members, have so judiciously planned, and by meritorious perseverance brought to its present state.

I have carefully perused the Rules and Orders, which have been prepared with much attention, and I think they are now sufficiently matured to be a guide and guard for the conduct and welfare of the institution. Judicious regulations are absolutely necessary in all societies, but I trust that in this, the good sense of the members will always prove that manners and moral feeling are superior to written laws, and will render my duty as President both easy and pleasant.

In foreign countries similar establishments are instituted by government, and their members and proceedings are under its control; but here, a different course being adopted, it becomes incumbent on each individual member to feel that the very existence and prosperity of the institution depend in no small degree on his personal conduct and exertions; and the merely mentioning the circumstance will, I am convinced, be sufficient to command the best efforts to the present and future members, always keeping in mind that talents and respectability are preferable to numbers, and that from too easy and promiscuous admission, unavoidable, and not unfrequently incurable, inconveniences perplex most societies.

He then worked hard to get the Institution accepted and operating, until by 1822 it had some 50 members (some from abroad), premises, and the beginnings of a library.* Rickman, in the 'Biographical Details' he gives in the *Life*, writes justly of the Institution, after 'it was consolidated by Mr. Telford's acceptance of the presidency. He immediately established the practice of recording in a summary manner minutes of their conversations, which did not fail to excite in the members attention to every object.' The Institution was taking off, but caused no diminution of the Smeatonians, but rather increasing association between their members[9]. It was incorporated by Royal Charter in 1828, by which time it had 137 members of all classes. When Telford died, aged 77, it had some 200.

---

* Interested readers may like to consult Sir Alexander Gibb, *The Story of Telford*, pp199–200, for what appears to have been something of a boycott by other engineers of the new Institution in its early days. The implications are peripheral to my own story.

Rennie had died in 1821, never having associated himself with the new Institution, and with him went what Telford may well have felt to be a Jessop–Rennie dominance dating from his early canal days. Indeed, before long Telford was to be actively associated with his son, later Sir John Rennie, who in his autobiography shows no bias against Telford personally.

Telford had now come out on top, with position and increasing influence to add to existing reputation. Of his early associates who knew the truth about the Ellesmere and Caledonian Canals, Simpson had died in 1816, Davidson in 1818. John Wilson, however, lived till 1831, but was soon to be fully employed on Telford's Birmingham & Liverpool Junction Canal. As soon as the Institution had acquired its new premises, Telford began to give it books and drawings from his collections, though most were not transferred until after his death. The latter included drawings of Pontcysyllte that were later lost, but not, as we saw earlier the drawing signed by Telford and dated March 1794, which had gone to the Reynolds' collection.

So we come to the famous ICE portrait showing Telford as an elderly man with the Pontcysyllte aqueduct, built so long before, in the background. Why not a more recent achievement, such as the Menai Bridge? As far back as 1805, in the papers accompanying the Oration, Telford had made his statement (p. 48). 'Pontcysylte Aqueduct . . . Thomas Telford, was the Engineer'. After his Highland visit of 1817, Southey wrote (p. 147) of Banavie and Pontcysyllte:

Telford it was, by whose presiding mind
The whole great work was plann'd and perfected;
Telford, who o'er the vale of Cambrian Dee,
Aloft in air, at giddy height upborne,
Carried his navigable road . . . .

His information could only have come from Telford. Then follows his choice of Pontcysyllte to stand behind his portrait, to be followed by the repeated emphatic 'I's of the first version of the *Life*. Have we here glimpses of an obsession, an insistence that 'Pontcysyllte is mine, mine, mine alone'; and glimpses also of inner uncertainty behind the emphases?

The portrait, painted by Samuel Lane, shows Telford seated, and in the background Pontcysyllte aqueduct, and in front the original

167

Cysyllte road bridge. It was exhibited in the Royal Academy in 1822, and titled 'T. Telford, Esq, F.R.S.E., President of the Society* of Civil Engineers'. The picture was formally presented to the Institution by Telford at a meeting on 7 February 1826, in these words: 'The President of the Institution, yielding to the Solicitation of many of his friends & from the expressions of respect he had received from the members, – and by the honour they had conferred in electing him as their President, presumed that what he had now to offer to the Meeting would not be unacceptable, he therefore begged to present A Portrait of himself for the Meeting Room of the Institution. It was Resolved ... that the Thanks of the Meeting be presented to the President for the gratifying present he has made.'

Southey, in his review of the *Life* in the *Quarterly Review* for Jan–March 1839, says of the Ellesmere:

> The two most remarkable of Telford's aqueducts are upon this canal; they are the most beautiful works of their kind in the kingdom. One is the Chirk aqueduct over the river Ceriog, the other the Pont-y-Cysylte over the river Dee. Mr. Lane has properly introduced them in the back-ground to his fine portrait of the engineer, and Mr. Telford himself had them both cut upon a large seal. Considerable difficulties were to be overcome in both.'

He is wrong: he must have mistaken the road bridge for Chirk aqueduct. I can find no trace of the seal.

Although of less significance, it is worth recording Telford's relationship with two other societies: the Royal of Edinburgh and the Royal (of London).

Telford was proposed for a fellowship of the Royal Society of Edinburgh on 1 March 1802. The minute book entry reads:

> Mr Stewart† proposed as a resident member of the Physical Class Thos. Telford Esq., Civil Engineer, Shrewsbury and was seconded by Mr Playfair and Dr Gregory.
> Mr Telford, by the hands of the Revd. Mr Alison, presented to the Society a copy of the plate representing the Ironbridge proposed to be built over the Thames.

His election followed on 31 January 1803. The date of proposal

* So in the printed list of Royal Academy Exhibitors, but one assumes that it had been correctly titled with 'Institution' when exhibited.
† Professor Dugald Stewart, in the chair at the meeting.

follows very soon after his commission on 27 July 1801 by government to survey and report upon Highland communications. He did so that same year, in the autumn returning, as Rolt records[10] to Edinburgh 'for a week's well-earned relaxation in the company of Professors Stewart, Gregory, Playfair and Robison★ of Edinburgh University'. Hence, presumably, the proposal by three of them.

This Scottish honour to the Scottish shepherd's son was never followed up. Telford seems to have taken no further part in the activities of the Society, even though he was often in Edinburgh, nor is there any reference to the Caledonian Canal, either in its minutes or *Transactions*. It seems somewhat of a snub to those who had so complimented him. Yet there was a sequel. In his will, Telford provided that his legacy of books, drawings, etc to the Institution of Civil Engineers should, if that body were discontinued, pass to the Royal Society of Edinburgh.

Finally, neither Jessop nor Rickman were ever proposed for membership or had any involvement with it.

As regards The Royal Society, Professor Skempton's and my best guess is that William Jessop was kept out by Sir Joseph Banks, across whose temperamental path he had strayed[11]. He seems never to have been proposed. Subsequent research[12] has strengthened this view by providing additional evidence of Banks' annoyance with Jessop.†

Yet when the Smeatonians had been reorganised in 1793 by a committee consisting of Mylne, Jessop, Whitworth and Rennie, they created a first class of members who were engineers, and also a 'class of Gentlemen, forming part of the Society, under the denomination of honorary members' and also as honorary members 'there shall be admitted various Artists, whose professions and employments, are necessary or useful thereto as well as connected with Civil Engineering'.[13] Banks was among those originally elected in 1793 as Gentlemen, and he became a regular attender at meetings.

John Rickman was elected to the Royal Society on 27 April 1815. He was proposed by Charles Abbot, for whom he worked, and is

★ Professor Robison had taught Rennie while the latter was at Edinburgh University, and later became a good friend.

† For an amusing account of Banks' 'Capricious exercise of the President's power with regard to exclusion', see *Philosophical Magazine* Vol. 56, No 270, October 1820, 'A Review of some leading Points in the Official Character and Proceedings of the late President of the Royal Society', by 'A Correspondent', an article that must have been written almost immediately after Banks' death in the same year.

described as 'a Gentleman well versed in various Branches of knowledge'. Telford's election did not take place until 31 May 1827, a month or two before his seventieth birthday, nearly ten years after the establishment of the Institution of Civil Engineers, and only a year before its Royal Charter. The citation reads: 'Thomas Telford Esq. of Abingdon St, Civil Engineer, F.R.S.Ed, a Gentleman eminently distinguished for his knowledge of Theoretical and Practical Engineering and whose name is intimately connected with many important national works . . .' The long list of supporters is headed, rather curiously, by Sir Marc Brunel, presumably as a matter of courtesy from a vice-President, and includes James Watt (the younger), Sir Charles Pasley, and both (Sir) John and George Rennie. Perhaps the late date of election owed something to the eddies that must have followed the ending of Banks' idiosyncratic exclusions.

Chapter 10

Rickman, Telford and the Life

Since John Rickman plays a significant part in my enquiry, a short biography is in order.[1]

He was born at Newburn in Northumberland in 1771, son of the vicar, the Reverend Thomas Rickman, who later retired to Christchurch, Hampshire. John went first to Guildford's grammar school and then to Oxford, gaining a B.A. in 1792. Then for some time he conducted the *Commercial, Agricultural, and Manufacturer's Magazine*, a tall order, one would think, for such a young man. In 1796 he wrote a paper showing how easy and useful a census of the population would be. Charles Abbot, later Lord Colchester, saw it, took Rickman for his secretary and used him to prepare for the first census Act, introduced in December 1800. Abbot then became chief secretary for Ireland in 1801; Rickman went too, and was made deputy keeper of the Privy Seal at Dublin. In 1802 Abbot became Speaker of the House of Commons, with Rickman still as his secretary. In 1814 Rickman was appointed Second Clerk Assistant at the Table of the House of Commons, and in 1820 Clerk Assistant, a post he held until his death in August 1840, aged 68. He married in 1805.

Clearly a man both industrious and orderly, he prepared an index to the statutes for House of Commons use, tackled the workings and results of the first four censuses from 1801 onwards, and wrote a number of parliamentary abstracts and reports. In 1803 he was made secretary to the Commissions for making Roads and Bridges in Scotland, and for constructing the Caledonian Canal, a post he retained until July 1830. In 1815 he became a FRS and in 1835 an honorary member of the Institution of Civil Engineers.

Rickman was an odd fish. A dry man, accurate to the point of pedantry, one would have said, were it not that he was a friend, sometimes a close friend, of such eccentric and intermittently respectable literary types as Charles Lamb the essayist, Robert Southey, Poet Laureate, and Samuel Taylor Coleridge, without having discernible literary taste. Himself seemingly happily married, he differed in that respect from his poetical friends, and Telford, his bachelor friend to be. Rickman came into Telford's life with the Caledonian Canal Commission, created as a consequence of Telford's survey of the Highlands in 1801. He held the post until 1829, and without question did excellent work.

Telford's relationship with Rickman got off to a shaky start – I quote from a letter to me from Mr Alastair Penfold[2].

> He was severely criticised by Rickman at the very beginning of the canal project for incorrectly drawing bills for canal expenditure and failing to keep a proper record of expenditure. The matter had arisen as a result of delay in obtaining the initial parliamentary grant. In order to maintain the credit-worthiness of the Commissioners, Telford had been forced to draw a bill for £1,000 from Mr Fraser, agent to the Bank of Scotland in Inverness, at an earlier date than was prescribed by the Commissioners in their August instructions. Before leaving London Telford had stressed to the board 'the necessity there would be for an immediate supply of money' and he had departed believing that he could draw money for the use of the works after the lapse of one month. The board demanded an explanation of his action, Rickman informing him that they felt more displeasure than they thought fit to express 'at the great irregularity and without previous or even accompanying explanation of your doing so.' All Telford's bills were refused by Rickman, the board having not directed that sufficient money to discharge these bills should be put to their credit account with the Bank of England. Rickman informed Telford that he 'had no discretion to exercise in this case, as I have no means put in my hands for paying them.' He concluded with a personal attack on Telford: 'if you wish to maintain the credit of the board uninjured by your own impudence, I suggest you have assets enough in Scotland.' The matter dragged on into the late autumn of 1803 . . . Telford's situation became extremely difficult in the Highlands and he requested a special board meeting on the 16 December 1803 to discuss the whole issue. Relations between the two men gradually improved after this date.

In the early days of initiating and planning the canal, Rickman had certainly met Jessop, probably several times. Also his biographer says '. . . he made more than one tour in Scotland in company with Telford . . . Telford and Rickman became fast friends, and worked

172

in complete unanimity . . .' for many years. Mr Penfold writes to me:

> It was a friendship that survived purely work contact. Certainly at the beginning of the Caledonian Canal period their politics were diametrically opposed, although Telford became more reactionary with age. There is no doubt that Rickman was a very useful contact for Telford, especially at the beginning of his career and that he strove to cultivate this relationship.

Rickman wrote to Southey on 22 July 1816: '. . . the Caledonian Canal; I ought not to forget that it is of unexampled dimensions, and consequently of much originality in its details, that my history of it in the Annual Reports is the first regular history of the formation of a canal, and a history, which with the adaptation of the appendixes, those of *workmen* and of *amounts*, I do not fear will ever be equalled. We must see this canal next year, taking Telford with us (or find him there) whom I think you may have seen here – a very able and very liberal man, whose plainness you will much like, an early friend of T. Campbell★ the Poet, and of Colonel Pasley – proof of his good taste; both of them respect him highly, and in his unostentatious manner I doubt not his friendship has served them much . . .'[3] In this letter we feel a change. How did Rickman know that the Caledonian was 'of unexampled dimensions' or 'of much originality in its details', except because Telford had said so?

So we come to the *Life of Thomas Telford, civil engineer, written by himself; containing a descriptive narrative of his professional labours; with a folio atlas of copper plates. Edited by John Rickman, one of his executors; with a preface, supplement, annotations, and index. London, printed by James and Luke G. Hansard and Sons, near Lincoln's Inn Fields; and sold by Payne and Foss, 81 Pall Mall, 1838, and its accompanying Atlas*, a book probably intended to fall into place in the long tradition of

---

★ Thomas Campbell (1777–1844), the son of a Glasgow merchant and educated at Glasgow University, first became known for his successful long poem 'The Pleasures of Hope', published in 1799. Among the acquaintances he then made were Telford, the Rev. Archibald Alison and the well known professor of moral philosophy, Dugald Stewart, all of whom became his patrons, in Telford's case so much so that Campbell named his eldest son, born in 1804, Thomas Telford. His second of 1805 received Alison's name. Col. (later Sir Charles) Pasley (1780–1861) was a distinguished military engineer who in later life became Inspector-General of Railways. His main link with Telford is likely to have been their origin. Pasley was born at Eskdalemuir, and seemingly educated by the same Andrew Little with whom Telford so often corresponded. Both were Scots, and considerably younger than Telford.

engineering autobiography alongside Perronet, Smeaton's *Reports* and Gauthey. In his youth Telford had ambitions towards poetry and literature, and these may have been remembered later, and tempted him away from a straightforward and properly documented account of his works.

Rickman in his Preface, gives this account of the origin of the *Life*:

> The present volume originated very naturally when Mr. Telford began to withdraw himself from undertaking new professional engagements, and, from a growing infirmity of deafness, felt himself uncomfortable in any mixed company. In this predicament, it was obvious to suggest to him, that, in his intended transition from activity to leisure, he might yet do good service to the public, without too much fatigue to himself, if by degrees he renewed acquaintance with all his accumulated papers, making such a selection from them as, aided by his own recollections, might display to the public all the great works executed under his superintendence, and all the improvements introduced by him during the third part of a century of extensive practice in his profession.
>
> Mr. Telford listened to this suggestion with much complacency, saying, that he had been thinking of the same thing, and had begun to arrange his papers; but that he felt himself out of the habit of composing accurately for public perusal; moreover; that as the work must be illustrated by many expensive engravings, and he might die before it was completed, he hesitated in resolving to undertake it. These objections were easily overcome, by promising him aid in the correction of his manuscript, if that should be necessary; and by undertaking that labour should not be wanting to make the book and its expensive plates available to the public, if he provided for that object in his Will....
>
> Thus encouraged, Mr. Telford became eager in his task, and proceeded with unexpected diligence, transcribing and correcting his first draft throughout. He also engaged his friend, Mr. Turrell, a very ingenious engraver, to work on the copper-plates...

Rickman goes on to say:

> ... the reader may be assured that due diligence has been exerted in augmenting the Appendix articles, now increased by about one-third in number beyond what Mr. Telford had actually collected for that purpose; but he had intended to augment them, and several of his surviving friends (it will be seen) have not withheld their assistance, especially such as extend the Narrative from the time of Mr. Telford's decease to the present day.

and adds that he has sometimes inserted an analogous word or phrase in the text, where it might not otherwise be understood by the general reader, and that notes have been 'inserted without hesitation, where they seemed in any degree pertinent to the subject mentioned in the text'. After the Preface follows a 'Descriptive Narrative of The Works of Thomas Telford', quoted as if in his own words.

This public statement differs from what was probably the truth, as written to Southey[4] '. . . I have almost placed myself under a vow – to write no Letters, nor do any superfluous or not indispensable act, till I had put into tolerable shape the posthumous work of Telford, which he commenced in 1830 under assurance that he dying in the Midst his labour should not be lost, nor the memory of his works perish. – . . . [Delays are now caused by the death of the engraver of the plates]. Three years have past, and Mr. Telford and his merit 'passing into oblivion' . . . I turn myself to fit up the M.S.S. for the Printer – and what with confused method in the text . . .'

In his will, dated 9 June 1834, Telford provided for 'The expence of the publication, describing the works in which I have been engaged from my earliest years; to be paid by his executors, who were named as John Rickman, James Hope and Alexander Milne. It was presumably because Rickman was an executor and had agreed to edit the *Life* that he was on 24 January 1835 proposed as an Honorary Member of the Institution. He was elected on 10 February. By then, on 27 January, the Council had made careful arrangements for the preservation and use of the plans Telford had left.

The Telford whose work Rickman had undertaken to edit and prepare for the press gives no reply to one's questions. L.T.C. Rolt found this:

Just three months before his death, a pencil drawing was made of Telford by William Brockedon. The thick curly hair has gone and the craggy face has softened, but it still tells us nothing; the dark eyes do not look at us; indeed, like a man in reverie they are not focused upon any external thing, nor do they betray any secret of the mind within . . . the portrait of this solitary, enigmatic and proud old man which emerges . . . is not a particularly lovable one; it is too lacking in warmth and sympathy – even in evidence of common human frailty – to claim our affection. Perhaps it is due to egoism . . . the man fails to move the heart;

perhaps it is simply because the private man so sedulously evades our question.[5]

From my own specialised study of a small part of Telford's active life, what have I learned? Unmarried and without children or, seemingly, nephews and nieces, half a normal man's life is closed to him; yet he does not fill it with achievement of his youthful longing towards poetry and literature, nor do his earlier political interests develop, though in his patronage of Campbell he perhaps recognised the poet he might have been. Not a Smeatonian, he is cut off from the benefits an able man derives from testing his ideas against those of others. The result seems to have been an abnormal preoccupation with himself and his achievements, and an excessive need for the active admiration of friends, men like Pasley, Campbell or Southey, all considerably younger than he, working juniors like Matthew Davidson, or that part of the engineering world over which he was later to preside in the Institution of Civil Engineers. Where among his intimates in any field of endeavour are his equals, in seniority or in ability? One perhaps comes to mind, von Platen, but again in circumstances where Telford was the superior. He is here in complete contrast to Jessop, elected to the Smeatonian Society in 1773, two years after its foundation, when only 29, and its secretary from 1778. Thus from an early age Jessop mixed with, and all his life knew well, most of Britain's good and great engineers. Moreover, even when he was especially busy with the canals of the mania, he could still give up time to be one of the committee of 1793 chosen to reorganise the Society, and later of that to publish Smeaton's *Reports*.

As I look again at the Brockedon drawing, it seems infinitely sad: that of an empty man haunted by his emptiness. Long years before, he had been given the choice all men and women are offered, to turn outwards to the world or inwards to themselves. Telford seems to have chosen the latter. Dante calls it *il gran rifiuto*[6], the great refusal. In the portrait Telford realises in old age what has happened to him. He chose egoism (Rolt's word), and that is what he has been left with: his ego – just that.

When Rickman took over the partly revised manuscript, he must have had a shock. There is no sign in the chapter on the Ellesmere Canal, the first in the printed book, that the author has used any sources at all, except insofar as he needed such figures as toll statistics. Those which Telford used on the Caledonian appear in

Fig 24: Pencil drawing of Thomas Telford by William Brockedon made three months before death.

the manuscript as annotations in the margin, not as integral parts of the text. Rickman must have realised that it was the work of an old, tired man hardly interested at all in the engineering works themselves, except very occasionally when a spark flashes and the writing suddenly comes to life, but rather in his own part in them. Moreover, probably only now Rickman saw Telford as a whole man, and not just as a great engineer in the Highlands.

As regards the Ellesmere Canal portion of the manuscript, Rickman probably had no personal knowledge of it, or of the part played by Jessop in its early history, and had derived his information from Telford. In a letter to Southey of 12 July 1838[7] a curious statement occurs, which may exemplify Telford's failing memory, or an abiding jealousy of Jessop even after some forty years, or Rickman's guesswork, in this case wrong. Southey has evidently asked him what Telford knew about canal inclined planes: he replies 'Telford was conversant in Inclined planes – & made several in a Canal which terminates in Coalbrook-Dale'. This was the Shropshire Canal, briefly mentioned in my opening chapter. Its history is set out in my *The Canals of the West Midlands*[8]. The records I have consulted show no link between Telford and the inclined planes, and his name does not appear in the company's minute books. Indeed, in his contribution to Plymley's *Shropshire* (see p. 19), Telford himself attributed the planes to Reynolds. The planes seem to have been the overall responsibility of William Reynolds with Henry Williams of Ketley in executive charge. The company's Bill of 1788 was got through Parliament by Jessop as engineering witness. He must have discussed the proposals with Reynolds before handling the Parliamentary proceedings, then not to have been further concerned once the Act had been obtained. The canal was opened in 1792, before Telford was engaged by the Ellesmere Canal's committee as General Agent.

As for the Caledonian, however, Rickman knew it all – none better. Yet back in 1822, in the curious matter of Southey's poems (see p. 144), Rickman had been prepared to allow public statements albeit in verse which embodied more than (or less than, as one looks at it) the truth.

What to do? The book could not be abandoned, because it was so prominently placed in Telford's will, with money made available. Neither could he, Rickman, desert it. He was committed by his promise to Telford when still alive, and implicated by being an executor of the will and to a small extent as a legatee along with his son. No fool, he must have realised straightaway that his position was impossible and yet that he had to carry out what he had undertaken.

He would also have to remember that until recently he had been Secretary to the Caledonian Canal Commissioners, whose views on the *Life* must be taken into account. Again, that there were many like James Walker, who knew much of the truth; they might be sympathetic to his problems, but only up to a point. Again, we do not know Rickman's personal opinion of William Jessop, but, though long dead, there were many who remembered him with affection and respect, and his personal papers presumably survived in his family's possession. One day they might be made available.

The importance given to the book in Telford's will gave Rickman a signpost. He could do nothing about the slovenliness and deadness of the writing, but he could improve and supplement it. Then, when he had done his best to make the *Life* presentable, it should be published as soon as possible. Once it had appeared under the name of the first President of the Institution of Civil Engineers, it must from the start be treated as the Authorised Version, and evidence that might be used to impugn it put in a dark corner.

The *Atlas* only claimed to 'illustrate' Telford's work. We do not know who made the final selection of drawings, or how it was done. If Rickman did so from Telford's large collection, he may not himself have known which were indeed his own. Certainly some seem unlikely.

The result of it all was a muddle, so much so that *The Times* obituary of Rickman says: 'he was the author of the prefaces and the arrangements of the population . . . also of the Life of Telford, the engineer ....', whereas the *Dictionary of National Biography* that 'he persuaded Telford to write an autobiography.'

Gibb[9] must have understood Rickman's difficulties: he says of the manuscript and of Rickman's editorial work upon it and the *Atlas*:

> The account was never completed, and the descriptions remained in a very disjointed form. They were ultimately edited and published by Rickman. It was a last tribute that he willingly paid to his old friend and colleague . . . But he probably also felt that he owed it to the Engineering profession, and to those great works in which chance had brought him to play such a considerable part . . . Nevertheless in spite of all, the, *Life of Telford* is not very successful. Rickman found it difficult to make time to finish it. More than four years after Telford's death it was still incomplete and he writes to his son the 'I postpone all things at present to urging on the Telford Book. This now', he adds, 'approaches to the sensation of an Incubus'! The result was that though very costly it did not do real justice either to the editor, or the subject; and it appeared several years too late to be of immediate interest.

There seem to have been few serious reviews of the *Life*. I have only found three: Southey's in the *Quarterly Review* for Jan-March 1839 (published anonymously), Sir David Brewster's in the *Edinburgh Review* for October 1839, and a more interesting one in *The Civil Engineer & Architect's Journal* of March 1839. Others either reproduced the text or are mere eulogies. Indeed, only two free copies for reviewers, including Southey's, were provided.[10] Others who wished to review it presumably had to buy it.

The *Journal* thought nothing of Rickman's ability as an editor:

> The subject had been so mutilated by the editor, that it is neither an autobiography nor anything else. The few snatches of Telford that are left, give a promise of what he was capable of effecting . . .
>
> He has warped the current of the subject to make room for irrelevant dissertations; the descriptions of works, instead of showing the minute care with which an author could dwell on his designs, are derived from the commonest sources, and a considerable part of the work is occupied with parliamentary reports, superannuated documents, Roman baths and other men's works.
>
> . . . (the editor) has produced a most admirable and agreeable confusion . . . Instead of this work being called the 'The Life of Telford, written by himself,' it should be called the 'Life of Telford with the part of "himself" by Mr. Rickman.'
>
> A large volume of plates is certainly given, but they contain so much that is trite, and so much that is useless, that they greatly derogate from the value of the mass.

One cannot but agree with the reviewer's general opinion of Rickman, but two amendments need to be made. The writer has not realised – how could he? – the nature of the original manuscript from which he had to start, and so is to that extent unfair to Rickman. On the other hand, he does not know that Rickman falsified both text and intention, and to that extent deserves even greater criticism.

The review is incomplete; one can only speculate why. But it includes references to the Ellesmere Canal, where the writer accepts that 'Telford's management of this complicated work was such as fully to justify (the management committee's) confidence in him, and he thus acquired new means of displaying the boldness and originality of his mind'. After which follow verbatim extracts from the *Life*'s account of the Chirk and Pontcysyllte aqueducts, without comment. The reviewer, however, really does know the Caledonian Canal, and thinks little of its treatment in the *Life*:

> The description of the works on the canal is meagre in the extreme; deficient in interest, and destitute of that practical instruction which such immense works might have afforded . . .

Finally:

The money and reputation of Telford have been lavished on it, but it shrinks in the scale when compared with such volumes as the 'Public Works of England', 'Railway Practice', the reprint of 'Smeaton's Reports', or the new edition of 'Tredgold's Steam Engine'; any one of which contains far more practical information, at half the cost, than this 'splendid work of Telford'.

I have in this book examined two chapters of the *Life* and the three existing texts, whereby readers can compare what Telford wrote with what was afterwards printed. They differ greatly, mainly because of Rickman's emendations or additions. Yet the published book's title is *The Life of Thomas Telford, civil engineer, written by himself.* This statement has been accepted from the beginning to our own days as true, from the time of Sir David Brewster, reviewing the *Life* for the *Edinburgh Review* who wrote: 'The whole work has been edited by Mr. Rickman in a way most creditable to himself, and highly honourable to the memory of Mr. Telford'. Yet even then, as we shall see later, there were some who realised something of what must have happened.

We are left with the puzzle of Rickman the man. Why did he allow his professional and personal integrity to be overridden?

Rickman's biographer quotes him as once having written to Southey:

From all novelists, tourists, anecdotists, beauty-mongers, selectors, abbreviators, et id genus omne, good Lord deliver us![11]

A friend wrote of him after his death: 'He was very anxious never to be deceived himself, and never to deceive others.'[12]

Nevertheless, we know that he recognised and indeed improved upon Telford's own selectiveness and abbreviations of events and time-scales, and in no case mitigated them, with serious results for historical truth. Indeed, he may have gone further down the slippery slope past ignoring towards encouraging the disappearance of inconvenient evidence. Is there any author who has not at some time looked gloomily at a newly discovered piece of factual evidence, wished heartily that he had never found it, and been tempted to ignore it or even, maybe, to mislay it?

Rickman may have done no such thing, yet one wonders when, and why, did Jessop's letters to Telford, probably over a range of ten years, on Caledonian Canal affairs disappear from the archives now deposited in the Scottish Record Office, which contain so much correspondence between Telford and others? We must here remember that the Caledonian was a state canal; public papers do not disappear as haphazardly as those of private concerns often do. It is possible, of course, that the letters remained with the recipients. If so, why did Telford, who preserved so many of his personal papers, not keep them? Mr Michael Chrimes* suggests they may have been taken by James Walker, then President and who had access to any Institution material, for his enquiry of 1839 into the then state of the Canal[13]. This is certainly possible, assuming the Institution ever possessed them. Whether it is likely I cannot judge. As for Jessop, who could equally have kept Telford's, they probably disappeared with all his personal papers (see p. 187).

Again, James Hope was law agent to both sets of Commissioners, those for the Canal and for Highland Roads and Bridges, and also another of the executors of Telford's will and, like Rickman a legatee along with his son. Hope's letter-books of 1803–38 are held in the Scottish Record Office. Those concerned with roads and bridges survive, but those covering the canal do not.

How comes it that the only letter from Jessop to Telford on Ellesmere Canal affairs (quoted on p. 36) survives because by mistake it was put with Matthew Davidson's papers, which were kept? Where are others that must have been written? Did Telford keep them? If so, were they made available to Rickman, and what happened to them?

One comes back to the 'why' of Rickman's actions. Was he so much influenced by Telford's personal magnetism? By deep affection over some thirty years? By a feeling that his hero must be allowed, right or wrong, full or empty, to be his own man? By pity for an old, lonely man near death who had yielded long ago to an impoverishing egoism when he might have been filled by personal generosity? Or maybe by them all, in proportions he himself could not disentangle?

To do as he had done was, he may have felt, the only service he could then do his friend. Telford was lucky to have as editor a man who was not an egoist, whatever we may think of his literary morals.

As we may by now have guessed, the *Life* sold badly. I have been unable to find the number printed. As early as 1842 Milne was

---

* Librarian of the Institution of Civil Engineers while this book was being written.

authorised by the Council in a minute signed by James Walker[14] to offer the remaining copies, including the copper plates, at 43s a copy. However, in 1844 the Institution was trying to buy back the remaining copies of the book, and also the copper plates, so that 'they might prevent the price of the work being reduced in the book trade', and 'to keep up the reputation of our first President's works'[15]. They were so bought, and copies then presented to suitable recipients. The 236 still remaining in 1845 were bought, along with the copyright, by James Walker[16], who succeeded Telford as President.

The *Life* was an unsatisfactory book, best forgotten – for whatever reason. Yet what happened?

Chapter 11

A Legend Grows

The foregoing pages have described a possible sequence of events which produced the *Life*'s two chapters about the canals upon which Telford worked with Jessop. The book had a lukewarm reception, but as those who had been present at the events it describe slowly left the scene, a change took place. The *Life* gained authority, because it existed, it was in print, it bore Telford's name endorsed with the words 'written by himself', and because there were no dissenting texts to raise doubts. So in footnotes or bibliographies of book after book from around the 1870s onward, the *Life* appears. Why should its authenticity have been doubted?

The legend that its accounts of the Ellesmere and Caledonian Canals were accurate began before the *Life* was published. In 1836 the first printed volume of the *Transactions* of the Institution of Civil Engineers appeared. It carried an Introduction, written by Michael A. Borthwick at the request of the Council, which included references to the great engineers of the past. He had been James Walker's assistant and private secretary from the late 1820s for eleven years. A *Memoir*[1] of Borthwick said:

> Early in the year 1833, he became an Associate of the Institution, and in 1845 he was transferred to the class of Members. He was indirectly connected with the Institution from a very early period, took a deep interest in its progress, and bestowed great time, research, and labour in editing the first volume of its Transactions, which was got up mainly through his exertions; all the articles in it underwent his anxious revision, while many of them were actually rewritten, and the Introduction was entirely furnished by him.

Here in full is what the Introduction says of Jessop:

> William Jessop claims to be more particularly alluded to. This excellent

184

man held an intermediate place in time between what may be considered the first and second generations of civil engineers, and he was the first of his profession that can be said to have been regularly bred to it. The pupil, and afterwards for several years the confidential assistant of Smeaton, he was reared in the best school, and it is not paying any niggardly tribute to his abilities and character, to say, that his subsequent career shed no discredit on his great master. His extensive practice consisted chiefly, though by no means exclusively, in works connected with navigation and drainage. The magnitude of his labours in these is attested by the improvements on the rivers Aire and Calder and the Trent during the time he held the appointments of engineer to those undertakings, by many of the numerous navigations intersecting the midland counties, by the great work of the Grand Junction canal connecting the central districts of England with the metropolis, by the inland navigations of Ireland on which he was the principal adviser, and by the City ship canal across the Isle of Dogs;-while in the Surrey iron *rail* or rather *tramway*, which, though not successful as a speculation, deserves notice as one of the earliest applications of this mode of conveyance to the purposes of public traffic, and in the conversion of the part of the river Avon through the city of Bristol into an immense floating dock, with the bridges and other structures accessary to it, he appears equally at home in other walks. These are the principal works which were more directly Jessop's; – he was besides consulting engineer of the West India Dock Company in London, and of the Ellesmere Canal Company, and indeed, from standing at the head of his profession for several years after the retirement of Smeaton, he was called in on most of the great schemes then in agitation, and also engaged in their execution, but they will be mentioned in connection with the men more immediately concerned in them, and to whom they are more usually ascribed, if not in a greater degree due. Any other course would evidently be quite out of place in a paper of the nature of the present, the object of which can with propriety only be to indicate generally the works on which different engineers have been employed, not to pronounce on the individual share in them falling to each.

There is one mistake; Jessop never held an appointment as engineer to the Aire & Calder Navigation; indeed he had little to do with it other than as builder of the Selby Canal early in his career. Otherwise it is a reasonable summary of his career, except that he was not 'consulting engineer to the Ellesmere Canal Company', but their principal engineer, and that it does not mention him at all in connection with the Caledonian Canal. One assumes, therefore, that the author had consulted Rickman, who had shown him the edited text of the *Life*. So quickly and so profoundly, therefore, as coming from the Institution itself, did the book begin to launder history. For instance, Sir David Brewster, reviewing the *Life* at length in the *Edinburgh Review* in October 1893, does not mention Jessop's name in connection with either canal. Nor does Robert Southey's article in the *Quarterly Review* earlier in that year.

The 'Memoir of William Jessop' was written soon after publication of the *Life* and published in 1844. Its author, Samuel Hughes, was roused to comment:

> It is singular that in the notice of Mr. Jessop in the first volume of the Engineers' Transactions, no mention is made of the Caledonian Canal, although it is perfectly notorious that he was the senior engineer of that work, that the plan and main features of its execution were settled by him even before consulting with Mr. Telford, and that during the progress of the works he continued to be the chief engineer, in which capacity he made an annual report to the Commissioners.[2]

It seems likely that the publication in 1836 of the account of Jessop's career in the Institution's *Transactions*, followed by the *Life* itself in 1838, had also led to protests from Jessop's family. It would be surprising if it had not. But when I enquired from the Institution whether they possessed any relevant correspondence from the post-publication period (i.e. 1838–42), I was told by the Librarian:

> I have been unable to trace any letters between the Jessop family or Samuel Hughes, and the Institution. Unfortunately there is a large gap in the correspondence between 1837 and 1841, and the letters in existence clearly represent only a small fraction of those received.[3]

During this time Samuel Hughes, collecting material for his proposed 'Memoir', applied to Jessop's family, who then consisted of John (1779–1869), a retired army man living at Butterley, William (c.1783–1852), in charge at Butterley and also an engineer with a reputation of his own, George (1796–1869), another engineer who had retired from India in 1839 to settle in England, and his one daughter, Sarah Scott (1788–1859), married to an East India Company maritime Captain. Of the four, William was unmarried, but both the other boys had children. It is likely, therefore, that William, John and George would have discussed the matter.

The result was printed by Hughes in 1844.[4]

The Author of this paper and the Publisher consider it necessary to state, that although they have not derived from the immediate relatives of the late Mr. Jessop any of that assistance which they ventured to expect, yet their thanks are eminently due to several valued friends of the author who had the happiness of personal intercourse with that distinguished engineer, and who have furnished them with numerous particulars, and allowed access to documents, the existence of which must be known to very few, and which would probably have never seen the light, but from the zeal which has actuated the Publisher in the production of these biographies.

Why was access refused? Not on this occasion alone, but presumably also to Samuel Smiles[5], the result being that no good life of Jessop was written, many of his achievements were forgotten, and eventually his personal papers themselves disappeared – though they may still exist. Why should three engineer sons refuse access to the papers of an engineer father who in his time was called 'from his experience and abilities . . . the first engineer of the kingdom'[6]. It cannot be because of anything discreditable in his private life: if there were, it would have been easy to remove the evidence. Only one plausible explanation occurs to me: the papers contained a good deal of material which might throw serious doubt upon the accuracy of what had been printed, first in the Introduction to the *Transactions* of 1836, then in the *Life* itself in 1838, under the great name of Thomas Telford, President of the Institution of Civil Engineers and Fellow of the Royal Societies of London and Edinburgh. Few families would be prepared to face such an uproar as might have followed. On the other hand, many at the Institution would have foreseen great embarrassment were Jessop's family to move towards opening his papers for study.

We can guess that an unwritten understanding was reached between the Jessop family and the Institution. Let the latter put the record straight in the most public way possible, and William Jessop's personal papers would disappear.

Three pieces of fence-mending by the Institution then followed. On 20 January 1846, addressing the annual general meeting of the Institution, Sir John Rennie, then President, in a review of British engineering, tried to meet the views of the Jessop family by giving what, through his father, he must have known to be a correct account. He put Smeaton and Brindley at the top of the great canal engineers, with Jessop first on his list of those that were to come later. Later, enumerating public works, he included (p.24): the Ellesmere by Jessop and Telford, with its magnificent aqueduct across the Dee near Llangollen, consisting of 19 arches 40 feet span, the centre being 126 feet above the Dee, with a total length of 1020 feet, and a width of 12 feet, the piers of stone, and the arches and aqueduct of cast iron; the Caledonian Canal by Jessop and Telford, 22 miles long, depth 16 feet, locks 40 feet wide by 172 feet long, 8 feet rise, top-width of canal 110 feet; locks intended for a depth of 20 feet; commenced in 1803, opened October 1820. . . .

Here, perhaps himself standing beneath Telford's portrait with Pontcysyllte behind it, Sir John is deliberately contradicting the *Life*, and also the Introduction of the *Transactions*, and establishing Jessop's position as Telford's senior on the Ellesmere Canal, including Pontcysyllte aqueduct, and on the Caledonian. To avoid having to say any more about Pontcysyllte at such a difficult moment, he then chooses to say nothing about aqueducts as a whole, and only to mention one other, his father's great masonry structure over the Lune near Lancaster.

A year later, after a paper had been read to the Institution on the Great North Holland Canal, there was some discussion about the Caledonian. James Walker, Telford's successor as President, took part, and after referring to James Watt's early report, says:

> After him came Mr. Jessop, who was for many years the engineer-in-chief. Mr. Telford, who was principally engaged at that time on the Highland roads and bridges, afterwards became connected with the canal as the executive engineer, and upon him developed subsequently the entire responsibility of the work.

Again a portrait of Jessop was in 1848 presented to the Institution by his son William. It is a copy painted by Edwin Williams about 1845 of the family picture (see p. 61).

These were brave attempts, but they were all too late, for in 1847 Edward Cresy's monumental book, *An Encyclopedia of Civil Engineering* was published: encyclopedic indeed, as it extended to over 1600 pages of small print with 3000 illustrations. The detailed and clearly-written sections with which we are concerned must therefore have been written much earlier, perhaps soon after the *Life* was published, and then supplemented from the Institution and other engineering sources. As concerns responsibility, here is Cresy on the Caledonian:

> In 1802, a survey of the coasts and the interior of the country was made by Mr. Telford, by order of the Lords of the treasury, for the purpose of

forming the canal from Inverness to Fort William. After Mr. Jessop's and Mr. Rennie's opinion had been taken on the possibility of effecting this desirable line of communication, an act was passed directing the works, and regulating the expenditure; Mr. Telford was appointed engineer.

and here on the Ellesmere;

The original plans for this undertaking were made by Mr. William Jessop . . . An act of parliament was obtained for this work in 1793. Mr. Telford was employed, and it was the occasion of his attention being more particularly called to the study of civil engineering.

Against Cresy's firm statements, and the increasing authority given the *Life* as time passed, fence-mending had little effect. Only in our own days, with the opening to students of so many more records and increased interest in inland waterway history, have efforts after truth begun to replace legend. This book is one of them.

ACKNOWLEDGEMENTS

The origins of this book lie with Professor Jack Simmons, whose essay, 'William Jessop, Civil Engineer' in his early book *Parish and Empire* first drew my attention to that great engineer, and with Professor A. W. Skempton, with whom I worked on *William Jessop, Engineer*, published in 1979. These two books, set side by side with the accounts of Telford's life given by Samuel Smiles, Sir Alexander Gibb and L. T. C. Rolt, raised the doubts that caused me to begin.

My debts are then to the helpful staffs of many public libraries, record offices and public bodies, especially those in Shropshire and Cheshire; the House of Lords Record Office and the Public Record Office (and its predecessor for my purposes, British Transport Historical Records); the Scottish Record Office and the National Library of Scotland; the Science Museum Library; the Ironbridge Gorge Museum Trust; the Institution of Civil Engineers, the Royal Societies of London and Edinburgh. I also owe much to the *Transactions* of the Newcomen Society, my long membership of which has brought me into contact with so many subject experts.

I owe a great deal to those brave people who have kindly read portions, or the whole, of the manuscript, sometimes more than once, and given me detailed comments and criticisms. Happy the author who has candid friends before publication rather than candid critics afterwards. Greatest of these is Professor R. B. Schofield of the University of Ulster, without whose knowledge and understanding I could hardly have written the book at all. There follow Mr A. D. Cameron, author of *The Caledonian Canal*, Mr Michael Chrimes, librarian of the Institution of Civil Engineers, Mr John Powell, librarian of the Ironbridge Gorge Museum Trust, who previously had photocopied for me the early drafts of Telford's

Life, Dr Barrie Trinder, of the Ironbridge Institute, who knows more than anyone about Shropshire's industrial past, and Mr Richard Dean, who not only drew my maps but long ago told me the whereabouts of Jessop's crucial Pontcysyllte report of July 1795. Responsibility for the final product, however, lies with me alone.

Others to whom I am especially indebted are Mrs Ailsa Maxwell for research in Scotland, Mr David Telford of the British Waterways Board, and Mr A. J. Conder, curator of the National Waterways Museum at Gloucester, who among many kindnesses has been twice to Scotland to search for and find Jessop drawings related to the Caledonian Canal. Also Professor R. A. Buchanan of the University of Bath, Dr Hugh Torrens, Mr Alastair Penfold, Mr J. H. Denton, and Mr Peter Wakelin.

Much also is owed to an old friend, Dr Mark Baldwin, who formerly worked with Professor Skempton at Imperial College, and is now, through M & M Baldwin, my publisher. Much also to my indefatigable yet always patient secretary, Mrs Susan Cadwallader, and most of all to my late wife Alice Mary, herself a historian and an author, who helped me with my contribution to *William Jessop, Engineer*, encouraged me in my earlier work on this book, and through long acquaintance felt great affection for William.

I am greatly indebted to Mr Richard Dean for drawing the maps and to the following for permission to reproduce illustrations: British Waterways Board, frontispiece, Nos 19, 20, 21, 22, 23; Harry Arnold/Waterway Images, 2, 13, 15,16, 17; Trustees of the Science Museum, 3, 14; Shropshire Libraries, 6; Dr Mark Baldwin 7, 10(a); Ironbridge Gorge Museum Trust, 8, 10(b), 10(c); Robert Jessop Esq. 9; Crown Copyright: Royal Commission on Ancient and Historical Monuments in Wales, 11; The National Portrait Gallery, 24.

NOTES & REFERENCES

Preface (pages 7–11)

1. Robert Southey. *Journal of a Tour of Scotland in 1819*. (John Murray, 1929).
2. The Telford-von Platen correspondence is in the Library of the Institution of Civil Engineers.
3. Copies of the Little letters are in the Library of the Ironbridge Gorge Museum Trust.

Chapter 1 (pages 13–19)

1. Charles Hadfield. *The Canals of the West Midlands*. (David & Charles, 3rd ed., 1985). pp 40–1, 150. Henceforward referred to as *CWM*. See also Peter Lead. *Agents of Revolution: John and Thomas Gilbert, Entrepreneurs*. (Centre for Local History, University of Keele, 1989). pp 62ff.
2. It is ironical that Telford, given his later work on the Caledonian Canal (see Chapter 6), here rails at 'Canals cut from Sea to Sea'. An Annandale Canal was indeed proposed in 1810, but not built. See Jean Lindsay. *The Canals of Scotland*. (David & Charles, 1968). pp 178–9.
3. Little letters, Library, Ironbridge Gorge Museum Trust.
4. *CWM*, p 151.
5. *Ibid*, pp 151–2.
6. *Ibid*, pp 152–9
7. See Charles Hadfield and A. W. Skempton. *William Jessop, Engineer*. (David & Charles, 1979) p 27. Henceforward referred to as *WJE*.
8. See W. A. McCutcheon. *The Canals of the North of Ireland*. (David & Charles, 1965). pp 69ff, and *WJE*, pp 17–18.
9. Such contact between Jessop and Reynolds is suggested in Dr Michael Lewis. *Early Wooden Railways*. (Routledge Kegan Paul, 1970). p 289.
10. MS copy of the original in Shrewsbury Public Library.
11. For Dadford, see index to *CWM*.

192

12. See Barrie Trinder. *The Industrial Revolution in Shropshire*. (Phillimore, 1981). p 117.
13. *Trans Newcomen Soc.* XXVI. p 174.

Chapter 2 (pages 20–45)

1. Some of the wording of this chapter comes from Chapter 7 of *William Jessop, Engineer* by Professor A. W. Skempton and myself. I now take sole responsibility for what is reproduced here, as for all additions or alterations.
2. Joseph Turner. *A Description of the Intended Canal from Shrewsbury to Chester and Liverpool*. (1791). In Wirral Central Library, Birkenhead.
3. Ellesmere Canal Proprietors' Minute Book, 7 November 1791.
4. Gell MSS, Derbyshire County Record Office, D258/50/139.
5. Ellesmere Canal Proprietors' Minute Book, 9th January 1792.
6. *Ibid*, 23 August 1792.
7. Ellesmere Canal Committee Minute Book, 23 September 1793.
8. *Ibid.*, 17 January 1794.
9. One of the signed drawings is reproduced on p. 103 of *William Jessop, Engineer*. This is held in private hands, the other five at the National Waterways Museum at Gloucester. The title of that reproduced appears in the Institution of Civil Engineers' list as in Telford's collection at his death, but is there attributed to him.
10. *Trans Newcomen Soc*, Vol 51, p 139.
11. *Aris's Birmingham Gazette*, 7 April 1794, repeated 14 April. *Eddowes' Salopian Journal*, 14 May 1794.
12. *WJE*, pp 261–2.
13. *WJE*, pp 44–6.
14. When we described Jessop's work on the Kennet & Avon in *WJE*, pp 244–5, Professor Skempton and I thought he had recommended a shortening of Rennie's original. We were wrong: he had proposed its abolition, but had been overruled on other than engineering grounds by the landowner, the Earl of Ailesbury. The present Bruce tunnel resulted.
15. William Reynolds' Sketch Book, Science Museum Library. A collection of engineering drawings by many hands, dating mostly from 1793 to 1796, mounted in a modern folio. Duncombe's drawing is No. 1.
16. MS report dated Shrewsbury, 14 July 1795 (Shropshire County Library, Shrewsbury, Deed No. 15025).
17. In this matter of water supply I have been greatly helped by Dr Philip M. Cohen's thesis, 'History of Water Management on the Welsh River Dee', 1986, Ph.D thesis of the University of Manchester Faculty of Technology.

18. Committee Minutes, 18 April 1804.
19. This letter survived by a fortunate chance among the correspondence from Telford to Matthew Davidson. Rolt in his *Thomas Telford* (Longmans, 1958) reproduces it, but wrongly dates it 26 June. Over a working relationship of some ten years, Jessop and Telford would have exchanged several such letters. Only this survives. Telford's probably disappeared with all Jessop's records, but what happened to Jessop's? (see chapter 11).
20. A rough copy of this report is in the Shropshire County Library, Shrewsbury, Deed No. 15031.
21. Report of 21 October 1795, loc cit, Deed No. 15035.
22. Gibb Collection, Box 80(6), ICE Library.
23. *Ibid*, Box 73(3), Estimates for Chirk Aqueduct.
24. Shropshire County Library, Shrewsbury, Deed No. 15036.
25. (Printed) Report of 24 January 1800, *loc cit*, Deed No. 15037.
26. Author's collection.
27. The estate was leased to William Hazledine until 1820 (*Salopian Journal*, 6 January 1813). If the lease were for twenty-one years, this suggests its beginning in 1799. If so, it ties in with the resumption of work on the aqueduct in late 1799, for now a local source for the iron work and skilled men to erect it were available. Hazledine, born in 1763 and therefore some six years younger than Telford, had his main works at Shrewsbury. Plas Kynaston was an offshoot that later became a considerable enterprise. The contemporary Bridgnorth foundry of William's elder brother John was quite separate.
28. Gibb Collection, Box 73(3), ICE Library.
29. Jessop had railways much in mind at this time, for he was just starting to build the Surrey Iron Railway.
30. Scottish Record Office, MTI/22.
31. Shropshire R.O. 543, Box 366.

Chapter 3 (pages 46–58)

1. Copies can be found in many libraries. I am using that from the Ironbridge Gorge Museum.
2. See *WJE*, pp 110–25.
3. *The Report of the General Committee of the Grand Junction Canal Company ... 4th of June 1805*, which incorporates *Substance of Mr Telford's Report of the General State of the Grand Junction Canal in May 1805*. In ICE Library.

Chapter 4 (pages 59–78)

1. Samuel Smiles. *Lives of the Engineers.* Vol 2. (1861).
2. Sir Alexander Gibb. *The Story of Telford.* (1935).

3. Her diary is in the Shropshire County Record Office.
4. The upper gates of the four locks at Frankton, and one pair of lower gates, were the first of cast iron. See *CWM*.
5. *Eleventh Report of the Caledonian Canal Commissioners.* Telford's report of October 1813. Rickman as Secretary to the Commissioners, knew the text of this report. See also p. 133.
6. 1842 Supplement to the *Encyclopaedia Britannica* (attributed to Robert Stevenson), says of cast-iron gates, 'Perhaps the first of these were constructed on Carron River, upon a small dock for the repairs of the Carron Company's ships . . .' (p.575). Carron was of course an iron-works concern.
7. Gibb, *op.cit.*
8. Gibb, *op.cit.* pp 27–30.
9. Alastair Penfold (ed). *Thomas Telford: Engineer.* (Thomas Telford, 1980).
10. 1987, David & Charles.

Chapter 5 (pages 79–114)

1. Douglas Hague and Stephen Hughes. 'Pont-y-Cafnau; the first iron railway and aqueduct?' *Association for Industrial Archaeology Bulletin,* Vol. 9, No. 4, 1982.
2. *Ibid.*
3. *Trans Newcomen Soc,* Vol. 2. 1921–22, pp 132–40.
4. *Trans Newcomen Soc,* Vol. 51, 1979-80, 137.
5. A second trough was added above the first, but I judge not earlier enough to concern us. Readers should however consult Stephen Hughes, *The Archaeology of the Montgomery Canal,* 2nd ed, 1983, The Royal Commission on Ancient and Historical Monuments in Wales, 19–20.
6. *The Iron Bridge* (1979) and *Trans Newcomen Soc,* Vol. 51, 1979–80, pp 140.
7. Ironbridge Gorge Museum Trust (Sir Alexander Gibb's transcript).
8. See Trinder. *The Industrial Revolution in Shropshire.* 1981. pp 51–2.
9. *Life* (see p. 65).
10. *Edinburgh Review,* October 1839. The quotation largely follows Telford's own wording in the *Life,* pp 29–30.
11. See full text, pp. 100–106.
12. Science Museum Library, Reynold's Sketchbook, No. 110.
13. Mr J. G. James, most knowledgeable on iron bridge history, supports 'a date not earlier than March 1795' in *Trans Newcomen Soc,* Vol. 51, p 140.
14. Peak Forest Canal Minute Book, 22 April 1795.
15. A very unreliable biography – J. Franklin Reigart. *The Life of Robert*

Fulton. (1856, Philadelphia) – indeed claims that Pontcysyllte was Fulton's.

16. Peak Forest Canal Minute Book, 23 April 1795.
17. R. Fulton. *A Treatise on the Improvement of Canal Navigation*. (1796) pp vii and 10.
18. R. B. Schofield, 'The Design and Construction of the Cromford Canal, 1788–1794'. *Trans Newcomen Soc*, Vol. 57, pp. 101–23.
19. Trans *Newcomen Soc*, Vol. 51, p 141.
20. *WJE*, Chapter 5.

Chapter 6 (pages 115–137)

1. Much of the wording of this chapter is taken from Chapter 7 of *William Jessop Engineer*. I now take sole responsibility for what is reproduced here, as for all additions and alterations.
2. For the Caledonian Canal generally, see A. D. Cameron. *The Caledonian Canal*. (Dalton, 1983, 2nd edn) and A. R. B. Haldane. *New Ways through the Glens*. (Nelson, 1962).
3. Appendix to *Third Report from the Committee on the Survey of the Coasts, etc, of Scotland*. Jnl of House of Commons, Vol 58, Pt II, 1007.
4. *A Survey and Report of the Coasts and Central Highlands of Scotland, Made ... in the Autumn of 1802, by Thomas Telford, Civil Engineer, Edin. F. R. S.* 15 March 1803.
5. Jessop's is Appendix 4 to the *Third Report*, op cit. 1014.
6. The student should note that this formal Bill is indexed in the Journal of the House of Commons under 'Scotland (Inland Navigation)'.
7. *First Report of the Commissioners for the Caledonian Canal*, 28 March 1804.
8. Letter, WJ to the Rt Hon the Speaker of the House of Commons, Newark, 9 August 1803 (Scottish Record Office, M.T.I/1/3)
9. Letter, TT to John Rickman, 27 September 1803 SRO, M.T.I./1/22).
10. Letter, WJ to the Commissioners, Newark, 29 September 1803 (SRO, M.T.I/1/26).
11. SRO, M.T.I./1/174.
12. SRO, M.T.I./1/46.
13. SRO, M.T.I./1/55.
14. *Report on the intended Inland Navigation from the Eastern to the Western sea by Inverness and Fort William; including Estimate of the Expense of completing the same*. By William Jessop, Engineer. Appendix C of the *First Report*.
15. SRO, M.T.I./1/174.
16. SRO, M.T.I./1/72.
17. Letter of 9 June 1804 to Telford. Appendix D of *Second Report*.
18. SRO, M.T.I./1/203.

19. In draft form, SRO, M.T.I./1/174. In final form, Appendix of *Second Report*.
20. See *WJE*, pp 257ff.
21. Caledonian Canal MSS 626.9 (412.1) ICE Library.
22. See *WJE*, pp 136.
23. Drawings listed are in the possession of the British Waterways Board, and not at present generally accessible. Others may well be yet unexamined. The last is in the Easton Gibb collection at the ICE.
24. For Jessop's docks, see *WJE*, chapters 5, 10, 11 and under 'Docks and Harbours' in chapter 12; for Telford's see Gibb. *The Story of Telford*. pp 308–14.
25. SRO, M.T.I./1/99.
26. 1,000yd of railway from Bersham, 2 miles from Butterley, ½ mile from Aberdeen.
27. SRO, M.T.I./1/113.
28. SRO, M.T.I./1/160.
29. In the possession of BWB.
30. SRO, M.T.I./1/162.
31. The list of drawings once owned by Telford, now in the I.C.E. Library includes: '*Plan and Elevation of a Swing Bridge for the Caledonian Canal. By W. Jessop*'. It cannot now be found.
32. The above from the *Third Report of the Commissioners*, 23 May 1806.
33. October 1806, Appendix C to the *Fourth Report*.
34. Clachnaharry, 14 November 1808. Appendix C of the *Sixth Report*.
35. SRO, M.T.I./1/174.
36. Inverness, 18 October 1809. Appendices B and C of *Seventh Report*.
37. Institution of Civil Engineers.
38. Estimate dated 18 October 1809 from Inverness, signed by both engineers, SRO, M.T.I./1/203.
39. 'Design for the Turning Bridge for the Caledonian Canal', signed W. Jessop 1810. (Drawing in possession of British Waterways Board.)
40. SRO, M.T.I./4/151.
41. Appendix B to *Eighth Report*.
42. SRO, M.T.I./1/203.
43. Appendix C to *Ninth Report*.
44. SRO, M.T.I./4/151.
45. SRO, M.T.I./5/102.
46. *Memoir*, op.cit., p 27.
47. *Tenth Report*, October 1812.
48. See *WJE*, p 269.
49. *Eleventh Report*.
50. Samuel Hughes, 'Memoir of William Jessop', *Weale's Quarterly Papers on Engineering*, 1, 1844.

51. Basis Catalogue, dated 31.12.1836, ICE Archives Register, No. 178.
52. See Jean Lindsay. *The Canals of Scotland*. (David & Charles, 1968). Chapter IV, and also briefly in *WJE*, pp 166, 181.
53. The above from Eglinton papers, SRO GD3/5/34 (for the April 1810 letter, GD3/4/182/1).

Chapter 7 (pages 138–152)

1. Orlo Williams. *Lamb's Friend the Census-Taker: Life and Letters of John Rickman*. (Constable, 1912). p 223.
2. *The Caledonian Canal*. p 90.

Chapter 8 (pages 153–161)

1. *WJE*, pp 166–7.
2. The article is by David Stevenson, the author of *Canal and River Engineering*. (1858).
3. See my *World Canals*. (David & Charles, 1986). p 79.
4. Joseph Priestley. *Historical Account of the Navigable Rivers, Canals, and Railways throughout Great Britain*. (1831).
5. *Lives of the Engineers*. Vol 2. (1861). pp 197–8.

Chapter 9 (pages 162–170)

1. For the Society of Civil Engineers, see A. W. Skempton and Esther Clark Wright, 'Early Members of the Smeatonian Society of Civil Engineers', *Trans Newcomen Soc*, 44 (1971-72), 23–47, 'Thomas Newcomen: a commemorative symposium', *Ibid* 50 (1978–79), 196–200 and *John Smeaton, FRS*. A. W. Skempton (ed), (Thomas Telford, 1981). pp 23–5.
2. *Trans Newcomen Soc*. 44, p 45.
3. Eglinton papers, SRO, GD3/4/182/1.
4. *WJE*, p 125ff.
5. *Ibid.*, pp 244–5. It has since been found that, as on the Rochdale Canal, Jessop had proposed to do away with a summit tunnel. A shortened one was built later at the insistence of the Earl of Ailesbury.
6. *Ibid*, p 83.
7. *Ibid*, p 119.
8. Samuel Hughes. 'Memoir of William Jessop'. *Weale's Quarterly Papers on Engineering*. I, 1844, p 1.
9. Skempton. *Trans Newcomen Soc*. 44, p 45.
10. Rolt. *Telford*. p 66.
11. *WJE*, p 268.
12. 'The Role of Sir Joseph Banks in the Promotion and Development of Lincolnshire Canals and Navigations'. W. M. Hunt, Open University doctoral thesis, 1986.

13. A. W. Skempton, 'Early Members of the Smeatonian Society' *Trans Newcomen Soc.* 44, pp 37–8.

Chapter 10 (pages 171–183)

1. See Williams. *Lamb's Friend the Census-Taker: Life and Letters of John Rickman* (Constable, 1912) and A.R.B. Haldane. *New Ways through the Glens.* (Nelson, 1962).
2. Author of *A Guide to Sources for a Study of the Life and Work of Thomas Telford.* (Ironbridge Gorge Museum Trust).
3. Williams. *Lamb's Friend*, p 181.
4. Letters, 21 September 1837, ICE.
5. Rolt. *Thomas Telford.* 1958, p 193.
6. Dante. *Inferno.* III, 60.
7. ICE.
8. 3rd ed. 1985, pp 152–9.
9. Gibb. *Telford.* pp 287–8.
10. Letter of 26 July 1838, Rickman to Southey (ICE).
11. Williams, p 9.
12. *Ibid*, p 17.
13. See Cameron. *The Caledonian Canal*, pp 107–12.
14. Institution of Civil Engineers minute book 28 June 1842.
15. *Ibid*, 19 June 1844, letter from C. Manby, secretary.
16. Indenture dated 21 July 1845, in the possession of the Institution.

Chapter 11 (pages 184–189)

1. 'Memoir of Mr. Michael Andrews Borthwick, M. Inst. C.E. by Charles Manby . . . Secretary.' I.C.E. Annual Report, 1856–7.
2. *Weale's Quarterly Papers on Engineering*, I, 1844, p 32.
3. Letter, 10 July 1986.
4. *Weale's Quarterly Papers on Engineering.* I, 1844, pp 25–6.
5. One result being that Smiles attributes the Rochdale Canal to Rennie and not to Jessop. See *WJE*, pp 126ff.
6. See *WJE*, preface, etc.

Index

The index covers pages 7–189 only. Modern spellings are used for place names. Page numbers shown in **bold type** refer to illustrations on those pages.